Extreme
FLOODS

Extreme FLOODS

A HISTORY IN A CHANGING CLIMATE

ROBERT DOE

SUTTON PUBLISHING

First published in the United Kingdom in 2006 by
Sutton Publishing Limited · Phoenix Mill
Thrupp · Stroud · Gloucestershire · GL5 2BU

British Library Cataloguing in Publication Data
A catalogue record for this book is available from the British Library.

ISBN 0-7509-4265-7

For Ginny and Terry

Typeset in 10.5/15pt Photina MT.
Typesetting and origination by
Sutton Publishing Limited.
Printed and bound in England by
J.H. Haynes & Co. Ltd, Sparkford.

CONTENTS

FOREWORD

There are many benefits associated with living near water but there are major risks too. Flooding has brought large loss of life and enormous economic and social costs to many parts of the world. It will continue to do so, because the world's increasing population adds to the pressures of living and working on river floodplains and in coastal areas. Changes in land use and climate may lead to an increasing flood risk in some areas in the future too. Consequently, it is vital we do not underestimate the risk that flooding poses to communities today and that we learn lessons from past experiences. Robert Doe provides the reader with detailed, fascinating insights into selected flood events during the past two millennia in and around the United Kingdom and northern Europe, with some discussion of events further afield. His chronology of extreme floods provides contemporary descriptions of the devastation caused by these events, together with valuable insights into why they happened and what can be done about them.

Robert Doe's discussion of extreme floods is based on an extensive range of historical sources, including diaries, chronicles and reports. Notable flood events associated with coastal surges are discussed, such as those which resulted in the loss of Old Winchelsea in East Sussex, and Tharlesthorpe in East YorkshŞire, and tens of villages and thousands of lives along the Netherlands coast during the frequent North Sea storm surges of the thirteenth to the fifteenth centuries. The author's detailed analysis of the coastal storm event of November 1824 and its impact on southern England highlights his readiness to probe the accuracy of some contemporary descriptions. He advises caution over the reliability of some early accounts without corroboration, and provides the reader with an extensive bibliography of his own sources, should he or she wish to undertake further studies of specific events. Throughout this book Robert draws on his extensive coastal research developed at Portsmouth University. Another example of his critical analysis is provided in the reconstruction of the time sequence of the onset of the flash flooding that devastated Holmfirth, Yorkshire, in May 1944. The chronology of extreme flood events is brought up to the present time through the inclusion of recent events such as the flash floods in Boscastle, Cornwall, in August 2004, the tsunami in south-east Asia in December 2004, the floods in Carlisle, Cumbria, in January 2005, and the inundation in New Orleans caused by Hurricane Katrina in August 2005.

Reading through this chronology of extreme floods will frequently prompt the reader to ask what would happen if a similar event were to occur today. Raising awareness that such floods may happen in the future is an important contribution of this book. Many communities remain vulnerable to the threat of flooding, with the potential for considerable loss of life and disruption. We need to seek reassurance from politicians, government agencies and others that accurate assessments of areas at risk from flooding are being conducted and are being communicated to residents, and that effective flood-management programmes are being implemented. As Robert concludes in this fascinating chronology of extreme floods, 'preventing extreme weather and associated flooding is impossible, managing the risk is not'.

Professor Derek Elsom
Oxford Brookes University

PREFACE

For over a decade I have researched, written and published flood-based content from around the world. I have witnessed floods first-hand and even waded through their cold, stormy waters but, thankfully, I have never experienced the true atrocities of personal loss or known fatality. Writing this book has proved enlightening, yet at times depressing. This discussion of flooding has made one thing very clear: one cannot understand the full consequence of flooding until one has been personally affected. It is very easy to assess global flood events from the comfort of an armchair, the luxury of multi-channel news reporting, the shocking headlines of newspapers and the bombardment of Internet sources, but it is to those who have endured it or have lost loved ones, their homes or their livelihoods that this text is a testament.

It was not until I set about compiling this text that I realised the full magnitude of the effect that water has had on the lives of so many for so long. We cannot live with it, we cannot live without it. But it is when it is whipped up into a tempest of disaster that our full attention is drawn to the catastrophe that it leaves in its wake. This text is not intended to sensationalise or shock, nor is it intended to be a definitive guide to flood-vulnerability – it would be impossible for one text to encompass all that. This book is designed to give perspective, to provide information on both historic and contemporary events that have changed both lives and landscape. Hopefully it will provoke some sobering thought and provide comparative information that can be used to put future extreme flood events into context, as one thing is certain: extreme flooding has been around since the dawn of mankind, and it is here to stay.

Much attention has been given to the assessment and validity of the sources and data discussed. As with any text that examines historical sources of evidence relating to physical processes, it would be excessively sanguine to expect absolute infallibility in reporting and recording. This said, a lot of work has gone into providing an accurate and reliable interpretation of events. It is hoped that the reader will find the resulting text stimulating, informative and interesting.

ACKNOWLEDGEMENTS

T he author would like to thank the following for their kind assistance and support: the Dartmouth Flood Observatory, Dartmouth College, Hanover, NH; the National Oceanic and Atmospheric Administration (NOAA); the Earth Observatory, National Aeronautics and Space Administration (NASA); the British Hydrological Society, Chronology of British Hydrological Events, University of Dundee; researchers at the Tornado and Storm Research Organisation (TORRO); the National Meteorological Library and Archive, Met Office, UK; the Environment Agency; Newcastle University Library; Gateshead Local Studies; the Deltawerken Online Foundation, Eindhoven; the National Information Service for Earthquake Engineering, University of California, Berkeley; the Bodleian Library, University of Oxford; the British Library, London; the British Geological Survey; Benfield Hazard Research Centre; the Dorset Coastal Storms Database; the Centre for Ecology and Hydrology, Wallingford; the Royal Meteorological Society; Bromsgrove Library, Birmingham and the US Geological Survey, Earthquake Hazards Program.

Appreciation is expressed to the following for relevant picture permissions: Stuart Morris; David Rydevik; Amy Carruthers; Arthur Mason; Deborah Taylor-Pearce; Kyle Niemi, the United States Coast Guard; Jeff Schmaltz; NASA; NOAA; the Science and Society Picture Library of the Science Museum; DigitalGlobe Inc.; the National Maritime Museum; the Schoenberg Center for Electronic Text and Image, University of Pennsylvania Library; and special thanks go to technical illustrator Christopher Chatfield. The author would like to thank Paul Brown, who co-authored Holmfirth flood research, Lance Tuffnel for newspaper transcriptions, and readers Martine Whittle and Samantha Hall, along with Christopher Feeney at Sutton Publishing for supporting and encouraging this text.

INTRODUCTION

There are bodies in the sea, there are bodies under mud, there are bodies everywhere.

(Hugo Chavez, President of Venezuela)

F loods kill more people and damage more property than any other natural phenomenon known to mankind. But what are floods, what induces them, what types of flooding cause the most damage and destruction, where do they occur and why are they such a big global killer? The concept of flooding poses many questions. Media reporting leads us to believe that we no longer experience just floods; instead we are experiencing extreme floods as a result of extreme events, events which sadly result in a large loss of life and widespread devastation. Maybe the 'extremity' is down to perception, reporting, heightened awareness and improved communications; perhaps it stems from more building on floodplains and habitation in areas at risk? Flooding from the sea and rivers, and rainfall flash flooding driven by thunderstorms, hurricanes, monsoons and typhoons are a fixture of daily reports around the globe. Whatever the causes, the consequences are profound. It is only when such forces of nature are experienced directly or indirectly that the full proportions really become apparent.

All over the world, the word 'flood' has many connotations. Even the word has changed: as an Old English word it was 'flod' or 'flud'; in German it is *Flut*, Dutch *vloed*, French *inondation* or *déluge*, similarly in Italian *inondazione*,

1

Table 1. *Locations of major global flood events in 2004*

Afghanistan	Chile	Hungary	Namibia	Slovakia
Albania	China	India	Nepal	Somalia
Angola	Colombia	Indonesia	New Zealand	South Africa
Argentina	Costa Rica	Iran	Nicaragua	Spain
Armenia	Croatia	Iraq	Nigeria	Sri Lanka
Australia	Djibouti	Ireland	Pakistan	Taiwan
Azerbaijan	Dominican	Italy	Panama	Tanzania
Bangladesh	Republic	Japan	Papua New	Thailand
Belarus	Ethiopia	Kazakhstan	Guinea	Togo
Bhutan	Fiji	Kenya	Paraguay	Turkey
Bolivia	Georgia	Korea	Peru	Uganda
Bosnia	Guam	(North and	Philippines	United Kingdom
-Herzegovina	(and	South)	Poland	United States of
Botswana	Northern	Macedonia	Puerto Rico	America
Brazil	Marianas)	Madagascar	Romania	Venezuela
Burma	Guatemala	Malaysia	Russia	Vietnam
Cambodia	Guyana	Mexico	Saudi Arabia	Yemen
Canada	Haiti	Mozambique	Singapore	Zambia

Source: based on data returns from the *2004 Global Register of Major Flood Events*, Dartmouth Flood Observatory, Hanover, NH.

and likewise in Spanish *inundación*. These words lead to a suitable definition around the English word we know as 'inundation', therefore suggesting that a flood is something that covers or inundates land through the action of water. But the textbook definition of flooding is not so clear-cut. It has many definitions and descriptions: 'an overflowing of a body of water, especially on land that is normally dry', 'an overflow of water, an expanse of water submerging land, a deluge', 'an overflow of water from rivers, lakes or sea on to dry land'. The words 'overflow' and 'dry land' are the key defining words. They signify the true essence of a flood: basically water that inundates, that overflows and encroaches on to land previously dry and unaffected by any such sudden water influence. But the definition is relatively limited, as it does not take into account damage or scale. One definition mentions rivers, lakes and sea but few mention rainfall, snow-melt or dam bursts.

The year 2004 was recognised as one of the worst in recent history for world flood events, as a result most notably of the large loss of life during an earthquake off the coast of Sumatra on 26 December, which triggered a series of deadly tsunamis. Indonesia, Sumatra, Sri Lanka, India, Thailand, the Maldives and Somalia were a few of the locations adversely affected. Approximately 200,000 people died, making it one of the deadliest disasters in modern history. There were nearly 200 major global flood events in 2004. A major flood is defined by the number of fatalities and significant damage to property and land, as well as the length of intervals between similar events (Brakenridge *et al.*, 2004). An alphabetical list of countries affected by major flooding in 2004 makes surprising reading (*see* Table 1).

Some eighty-two countries and barely a continent unaffected! Tropical storms, depressions, typhoons, hurricanes and cyclones influenced this flood count. The main culprits were: tropical storms Winnie and Gaston, tropical depression Merbok, typhoons Muifa, Songda, Nock-ten, Tokage, Meari, Haima, Chaba, Megi, Rananim, Mindulle and Tingting, hurricanes Jeanne, Ivan and Frances and cyclones Fay, Grace, Gafilo and Monty. If we look at some of the causes more closely, it becomes apparent why certain areas of the world are more prone to flooding.

STORMS

A tropical storm is an organised weather system of strong thunderstorms with a defined circulation and sustained wind speeds of 39–73mph (33–63 knots); essentially it is a type of low-pressure system which forms over the warm waters of the tropics. On formation, the storm is assigned a name. The reason storms are named is to enhance the communication of forecasts and warnings between meteorologists and the general public. Historically, storms were named after the saint's day on which they occurred, for example 'Santa Ana', which struck Puerto Rico on 26 July 1825 (NOAA-NWS, 2005b). During the Second World War, tropical storms were informally given women's names after the girlfriends and wives of US Army Air Corps and Navy meteorologists who monitored storms over the Pacific; then in 1979 men's names were introduced. Today, names are devised by an international committee of the World Meteorological Organization.

The intense, heavy and prolonged rainfall from tropical storms creates a serious flood risk. To put such quantities into perspective, a weather station in north-east Houston, Texas recorded over 26in (660mm) of rain in almost ten hours as a result of Tropical Storm Allison in June 2001 (Risk Management Solutions, 2001). This is a staggering amount in a short time, considering that the average annual rainfall for Houston is around 42in (1,066mm). Allison produced well over half the annual rainfall in that ten hours. The remnants of Tropical Storm Gaston produced heavy rain over South Carolina at the end of August 2004 and weakened into a depression as it moved into North Carolina and Virginia. Despite maximum wind speeds of around 40mph (35 knots), there was record-breaking flooding. In South Carolina and Virginia, bridges were washed away and flood water 10ft (3m) deep was reported in some towns. A more intense tropical storm, Winnie, occurred towards the end of November and into December 2004. This produced high winds, torrential rains and flash floods, which triggered landslides in the northern Philippines. The flash flood-induced landslides were enhanced by deforestation, and this led to around 700 deaths with hundreds unaccounted for as logs and mud covered villages.

As a tropical storm reaches wind speeds of 74mph (64 knots) or greater, it is classified a hurricane. The word 'hurricane' does not have a clear origin; some legends suggest association with the West Indies or Caribbean, based on a word *huracán* (or Taino *hurákan*), meaning 'great wind'. Others suggest that it originated from *hunrakan* (or *hunraken*), a Mayan god of storms. When the first humans made him angry, he swept them away in a violent flood. Therefore, the word has a long association with great winds and floods all around the world.

The 2004 hurricane season was classed as one of the most active and costly Atlantic hurricane seasons on record and this was largely the result of hurricanes Frances, Ivan and Jeanne (FEMA, 2005). At the time of writing, the 2005 hurricane season is under way and is also looking like being a record-breaker in many ways. Hurricane Ivan (4 to 24 September 2004) had a long, destructive track affecting Grenada before crossing the Caribbean Sea, passing close to the Jamaican coast, Grand Cayman and Cuba. Ivan then moved into the eastern Gulf of Mexico as it continued on a track towards the north-north-west, making landfall near Gulf Shores, Alabama, before turning

4

east and affecting Florida. Its passage produced torrential rain and flash flooding as well as a storm surge of between 10 and 15ft (3–4.5m), made worse by the storm's arrival at high tide.

The storm surge was accompanied by large, battering waves along the western Florida panhandle and Alabama coastline. Even the remnants of Hurricane Ivan produced up to 9in (228mm) of rain across western Pennsylvania on 17 September 2004, which triggered massive flooding and mudslides. Soil previously saturated by a wet summer caused the Delaware river at Montague, New Jersey, to rise 20ft (6m) in twelve hours and produce the third-largest flood in recorded history at this location (US Geological Survey, 2005). The flood impacts as a direct result of Hurricane Ivan and its remnants are too numerous to mention in one short text; press headlines at the time – 'highest levels in 40 years', 'worst floods since 1959' – indicated the enormity of this devastating weather system. One report was truly staggering: Ivan produced the highest swell-wave ever recorded. As Hurricane Ivan approached the US Gulf Coast, it passed over an array of sea-floor sensors deployed by the US Naval Research Laboratory to measure water pressure. The network detected what was thought to be the largest wave ever measured by instruments: the distance between the crest and trough was a staggering 91ft (27.7m). In fact, it was thought that the instruments missed some waves that were as high as 132ft (40m) (Wang *et al.*, 2005). The previous record was 86ft (26.2m), recorded in the Atlantic in December 1972. Mid-ocean storm waves usually lose energy and dissipate relatively quickly; however, they do pose a significant threat to shipping and small islands. These types of wave events do create some concern for the future, as it has been suggested that a volcanic eruption on the Cumbre Vieja volcano at La Palma in the Canary Islands could send a large part of the island into the sea, triggering a wall of water some 2,000ft (650 m) high that would surge towards the east coast of the United States (Ward and Day, 2001). In theory, this wave would get smaller as it crossed the Atlantic but would rise again as it hit the American continental shelf. If this does happen, it will have devastating consequences for low-lying areas, for example Florida, where the wave could inundate the mainland for several miles inland. Only time will tell.

Barely a week after Ivan, Hurricane Jeanne (13 to 28 September 2004) brought heavy rainfall and flooding to Puerto Rico, the Dominican Republic and Haiti. Sources put the death toll at over 3,000, the majority of which occurred in the coastal city of Gonaïves, Haiti, where around 80,000 of the city's 100,000 residents were adversely affected. Haiti is one of the poorest countries in the western hemisphere, with 80 per cent living below the poverty threshold, so when an extreme flood event of this magnitude occurs, the suffering and recovery are long-drawn-out. Incredibly, Hurricane Jeanne did not strike Haiti directly, but its passage was large enough to cause severe mudslides and flooding. Jeanne continued strengthening as it headed west over the Bahamas towards a landfall along the Florida coast, where early on the 26th, the centre of Jeanne's 60-mile-wide eye crossed the Florida coast near Stuart, with maximum winds at the time of landfall estimated at around 120mph (104 knots). The winds whipped up a storm surge and the US National Weather Service Hurricane Prediction Center reported a surge of 3.8ft (1.15m) above normal astronomical tide levels at Trident Pier, Port Canaveral, Florida, about an hour after Jeanne made landfall.

A RARE HURRICANE

In the Atlantic Ocean north of the equator, hurricane season begins in June and is usually over by the end of November. In the Atlantic south of the equator there is no hurricane season because, as any meteorologist will confirm, there have been no known occurrences in this region. As a meteorologist at NASA's Goddard Space Flight Center explained (Muirhead, 2004, p. 374):

> Hurricanes require a perfect blend of conditions. Waters must be warm, wind shear must be low, and a disturbance, such as thunderstorms, must jump-start storm formation. The shear component is particularly detrimental. If the wind increases too quickly with altitude or changes direction, the hurricane is torn apart before it can organise. With its cooler waters, frequent wind shear, and lack of seedling thunderstorms, the South Atlantic just is not a place where scientists or sailors keep watch for hurricanes.

But the climate is changing, and this brings a whole new dimension to storms and flood vulnerability in the South Atlantic. It was with much amazement that meteorologists watched the first-ever recorded hurricane develop off the coast of Brazil during March 2004. A NASA hurricane researcher said:

> This really caught everyone off guard. Hurricanes are not supposed to be in that part of the world. Weather satellites have been circling Earth for more than 40 years and during that time they have spotted hurricanes in the northern Atlantic Ocean, and on both sides of the equator in the Pacific and Indian Oceans, but never before in the South Atlantic.

The storm reached hurricane strength as it neared the coast of Brazil and made landfall in the state of Catarina, hence its designated name, on 27 March 2004. Civil defence officials in Brazil said that at least three people were killed and thirty-eight injured.

Climate models are unable to project accurately how hurricanes will change in the future (McCarthy *et al.*, 2001). In theory, hurricane intensity should increase with increasing global mean temperatures, but research on the frequency of intense hurricanes has shown no clear increase (Landsea *et al.*, 1996). However, more recent research suggested that hurricane intensities may have increased in recent decades as the tropical oceans have warmed. Emanuel (2005) reported that the accumulated annual duration of storms in the North Atlantic and western north Pacific have increased by around 60 per cent since 1949, though this may partially reflect changes in reporting practices. Webster *et al.* (2005) suggested that an increase has been seen in the number of hurricanes reaching categories 4 and 5. The largest increase has occurred in the north Pacific, Indian and south-west Pacific Oceans, and the smallest percentage increase occurred in the north Atlantic Ocean. Therefore, in a world made warmer by increased greenhouse gases, the strongest hurricanes under present climate conditions may increase in intensity over the next century and possess more intense rainfall, leading to greater episodic flooding.

TYPHOONS AND SUPER-TYPHOONS

In the Pacific Ocean (west of the International Date Line) typhoons produce strong winds, torrential rain and flooding. The word 'typhoon' has many associations, including the Cantonese *t'ai fung* (great wind) and the Persian *tufin* (smoke), and is also linked to the Greek word *typhoeus*. Typhoons have winds greater than 74mph (64 knots) and are classified a super-typhoon when greater than 149mph (129 knots). Typhoon Tip was the most intense and largest typhoon on record. Forming in early October 1979 it soon became a super-typhoon with winds at 190mph (165 knots) and a central pressure at 870mb, the lowest barometric pressure ever recorded from a tropical cyclone (NOAA-NWS, 2005a). It caused widespread flooding across most of Japan, where the agricultural and fishing industries sustained heavy losses. Flooding from heavy rain also breached a fuel-retaining wall at Camp Fuji, west-north-west of Yokosuka. The fuel caught fire, causing sixty-eight casualties, including eleven deaths among the US Marines stationed there.

The Naval Oceanography Command Center's Joint Typhoon Warning Center report (1979) of this event makes interesting reading. It explained that, considering the size and strength of Super Typhoon Tip, the Western Pacific fared well, as the maximum intensity was reached while the system was still far from any inhabited areas, but the potential for mass destruction was always there. It may seem strange, but Tip was also a thing of great beauty. One of the aerial-reconnaissance weather officers stated, shortly after returning from an airborne mission:

This is unquestionably the most awe-inspiring storm I have ever observed. In the 2+ hours that transpired between the first and second fixes, the moon had risen sufficiently to shine into the eye through an 8 nautical mile clear area at the top of the eyewall. To say it was spectacular is totally inadequate . . . 'awesome' is a little closer.

For Japan, 2004 was a record-breaking year for typhoons, with ten making landfall. Typhoons Songda, Tokage, Chaba and Meari were a few names to blame. Typhoon Chaba (which formed on 18 August 2004) quickly intensified into a super-typhoon with, at peak, sustained winds of 178mph (155 knots) producing a storm surge of approximately 18ft (5.5m) to the Northern Mariana Islands, in the north Pacific Ocean. The storm caused widespread damage and extensive flooding, sparking an international relief effort. When it struck Japan on 30 August it was responsible for around thirteen deaths, flooding 13,000 homes and severing electricity to more than 300,000 households.

CHINA'S SORROW

In a closer examination of flood vulnerability, two main flood sources present themselves: floods from rivers and floods from coastal (and estuarine) sources. Floods from rivers are influenced by rainfall, snow- and ice-melt, failure of dams and blockages such as landslides. Rainfall is one of the key components, as heavy or prolonged rain can cause a river's depth to increase, exceeding the capacity of the channel and natural banks, leading to an inundation of the floodplain or surrounding land. The topography is a critical influence, especially if the soil has poor water retention or the rainfall exceeds the ground's ability to absorb this sudden influx. In this situation, high-intensity rainfalls, especially over short periods of time, can lead to sudden flash flooding, which is greatly influenced by geology and landscape. One of the most flood-prone river environments of the world, is the middle and lower reaches of the Yellow and Yangtze rivers in China. The Yellow River (Huang He) is approximately 3,395 miles (5,464km) long, the second longest river in China after the Yangtze (at about 3,915 miles or 6,300km, the Yangtze is the longest river in Asia and the third longest in the world, after the Nile and the Amazon). These rivers have suffered flooding of staggering proportions, particularly the Yellow River, which is known as 'China's sorrow'. It is easy to see why, as a flood in 1642 was believed to have killed around 300,000 people. But worse was to come in 1931 after weeks of unremitting rain. It produced a flood event considered to be the deadliest natural disaster in recorded history (discounting pandemics), or at least almost certainly of the twentieth century.

There was a prolonged drought in China between 1928 and 1930, and when the heavy and prolonged rains arrived in July and August 1931 the most terrible of catastrophes occurred. The estimated number of people killed by the Yellow and Yangtze river floods ranged between 140,000 and 850,000, but the total death toll was thought to be well over 3 million people as a result of famine and disease (Clark, 1983). It has been suggested that over 50 million people were affected by these floods, around a quarter of the population of China. These facts and figures show the startling consequences of such inundations. However, press reports in early October 2005 indicated that the Yellow River is in another period of drought, a drought suggested to be far worse as a result of distinct rises in temperature. The Tibetan Plateau, known as the 'roof of the world' and the source of both the Yangtze and Yellow rivers, has seen an overall temperature rise of nearly one degree Celsius during the past thirty years. The rise in temperature has resulted in a reduction of the glacier area in the region by 17 per cent in 2000, compared with figures recorded in 1966 (Yongjian *et al.*, 2005). The Greenpeace-led report said, 'From here it is a domino effect that harms the flora, fauna, landscape and people of the Yellow River source region – and ultimately the river itself. Water shortage and reduced run-off at the source will have far-reaching impacts upon the economy, society and people's life, not only in the source region but in the middle and low reaches of the Yellow River.' In contrast, there are only a few areas of the world that are completely free from the perils of flood water. One is the Atacama Desert, Chile, which runs from the Pacific Ocean to the Andes mountains, where the average annual rainfall is less than 0.5in (13mm) provided only by the occasional squall, but some areas of the desert have been rain-free for centuries.

FEARED FLASH FLOODS

In mountainous or steep-sided valley environments an enhanced danger from flash flooding is known to exist. These environments are also more susceptible to landslides and mudslides, and those which are steep, bare of vegetation and with poor soil saturation will be more vulnerable. Such conditions had catastrophic consequences in Venezuela in December 1999, when torrential rain triggered landslides in an area which separated Caracas from the Caribbean coast. The National Ocean and Atmospheric Administration (NOAA) estimated rainfall amounts of 11–18in (300–480mm) over the towns of Maiquetia and La Guaira, north of Caracas, between 15 December and 17 December. The exact death toll could not be fully ascertained but it was thought to be as high as 20,000. 'There are bodies in the sea, there are bodies under mud, there are bodies everywhere,' Venezuelan president Hugo Chavez tragically stated after touring parts of the Caribbean coast.

Flash floods are feared throughout the world because of their sudden and unpredictable nature. A flash flood is defined as a rapid flooding of low-lying areas by rivers and streams, caused by intense rainfall often associated with thunderstorms, or multiple training thunderstorms. In meteorology, training storms are a successive series of showers or thunderstorms that move repeatedly over the same area. This happens when a band of rain or storm cell forms along a stationary weather front and moves down the length of the front, while the front is stalled. A similar situation produced the Boscastle, UK, flash floods in August 2004. These severe thunderstorms can be violent weather systems that produce gusty winds, lightning, hail and very heavy rain. They are usually of short duration and last only one or two hours, but the high-intensity rainfall can create huge volumes of water capable of destroying towns and sweeping away anything in its path.

Flash floods can also be caused by other influences, including rapid snow-melt, failure of natural or man-made defences, ice jams or freshets. The term 'freshet' is commonly used to describe a spring thaw resulting from snow- and ice-melt in rivers. They are common in North America, particularly Canada, where the rivers are frozen during the winter and then, with the spring, the thaw leads to a mass inundation of water into the floodplains. This is often influenced by ice jams and a temporary damming effect that block the normal course of the river. Dams have also been known to cause major flash floods. If a dam exceeds its volume, or indeed breaks, a devastating flood will ensue. One of the most notable was in Johnstown, Pennsylvania in 1889, when the South Fork Dam collapsed some 10 miles (16km) upstream from the city during heavy rains. Over 2,000 people died as a result of the flood and a subsequent fire that raged through the debris. More recently, the Banqiao Reservoir Dam and Shimantan Reservoir Dam were among sixty-two dams in Zhumadian prefecture in China's Henan province that failed catastrophically in 1975 during a typhoon. Approximately 26,000 people died as a direct result of the flooding, and a further 140,000 died during subsequent epidemics. It is interesting to note that Banqiao Reservoir Dam was designed to survive a once-in-a-thousand-year flood (12.1in or 306mm of rainfall per day). However, in August of 1975 a once-in-two-thousand-years flood occurred as a result of an intense typhoon, and after several days a new record was set at 6.3in (160.4mm) of rainfall per hour and 64in (1,631mm) per day, while the average annual precipitation was about 31in (800mm) (Yi Si, 1998). The sluice gates were not able to handle the overflow of water, partially as a result of sedimentation blockage. The flood waters caused a large wave, 6 miles (10km) wide and 10–23ft (3–7m) high, which rushed downwards into the plains below at nearly 30mph (26 knots).

Floods that occur in very hot, dry conditions are enhanced by the hard, dry and encrusted ground. In very flat areas, a ponding of water can form during sudden and prolonged heavy rainfall. Typically this is more common in arid and semi-arid environments. If these areas are very level, with few or no clearly defined channels, the water will be influenced and move with the local topography. In the context of surface ponding, it is important to consider the impact of urban flooding as a result of storm water run-off and inadequate drainage. In towns and cities, the storm water systems must cope with the level of water, particularly from high-intensity rainfall events, as best they can. But if such systems are ageing or inadequately designed to cope with extreme conditions, this will cause problems. The limitations of London's storm water system became apparent in August 2004, when the equivalent of the average rainfall for the month fell in north-west London in just two hours. This lead to over half a million tonnes of raw sewage being discharged via storm relief overflows into the Thames. The pollution killed many thousands of fish, the worst fish mortality in ten years, and rowers and canoeists were hospitalised with gastroenteritis (Brown and Jones, 2004).

STORM SURGES

When we consider the risk of flooding from the sea, then a much wider picture of flood vulnerability is obtained. Storm surges and tsunamis are all capable of creating floods of extreme proportions. Storm surges are one of the most notorious flood sources, affecting coastlines all around the world; they are known for their extensive flooding, misery and, sadly, great cost in lives.

The term 'storm surge' refers to an increase in water level in addition to normal tidal variations. Essentially it is meteorological in origin and has its origins in the passage of a low-pressure weather system with strong winds piling water against a coastline. This is also influenced by the depth of seabed features and the topography of the coast in question. Severe flooding is more likely to occur when a storm surge coincides with high spring tides and it is common for a storm surge to accompany hurricanes, typhoons and cyclones. A devastating storm surge in the Bay of Bengal during November 1970 created one of the worst natural disasters of the twentieth century. The Bay of Bengal is one of the major centres of the world for the breeding of tropical storms. The low-lying Bangladesh coast is also located in this bay and the rather flat topography makes it particularly vulnerable to flooding. Bangladesh is no stranger to storm surges, with notable events in 1737, 1864, 1876 and 1897, but it was a storm surge during the night of 12 November 1970 that produced, on a high tide, a surge of 16 to 30ft (5–9m). This led to some 300,000 deaths, which later rose to a reported 500,000 (Clark, 1983).

The 'largest storm surge ever recorded' occurred in March 1899 during Tropical Cyclone Mahina, which passed through northern Queensland, Australia. Mahina was a category 5 cyclone, the most powerful of the tropical cyclone severity categories. It was later dubbed 'the Bathurst Bay Hurricane' (near Princess Charlotte Bay, Cape York) and went on to create a surge that was around 42ft (12.8m), although some sources suggested 48ft (14.6m). The Emergency Management Australia (EMA) Disasters Database (2004) described how:

> . . . tonnes of fish and some dolphins were found 50 feet [15m] above sea level up to several miles inland and rocks were embedded in trees. On Flinders Island, dolphins were found 50 feet [15m] up on the cliffs. On that night of the 4th March, Constable J.M. Kenny reported that a 48 feet [14m] storm surge swept over their camp at Barrow Point (south of Cape Melville) atop a 40 feet [12m] high ridge and reached 3 miles [5km] inland, the largest storm surge ever recorded.

Sadly, there was large-scale loss of life, as more than 300 crew members from a pearling fleet drowned on the shores and the Great Barrier Reef, and more than 100 Aborigines died, some in the back-surge of water while trying to rescue shipwrecked men.

Coastal areas are not static entities. In theory, the coastal zone floods daily as the rotation of the moon around the Earth causes the sea level to rise and fall, producing what we know as tides. It is the magnitude of these tides that is a primary focus in assessing local flood vulnerability during storms, especially when it is amplified as a result of a storm surge. One of the most notorious storm surges on record for the North Sea occurred on 31 January and 1 February 1953. A combination of a high spring tide and a depression to the south of Iceland deepened and tracked down the North Sea. The coastlines of Lincolnshire, Norfolk, Suffolk, Essex and Kent were severely flooded. As a result, over 386 sq miles (100,000 hectares) of eastern England were flooded and 307 people died. In the Netherlands, dykes burst and officials put the death toll at over 1,800 people. The flood covered around 9 per cent of all Dutch agricultural land.

The tidal amplitude was less influential in 1954 when Hurricane Carol arrived shortly after high tide, with storm surge levels between 5 and 9ft (1.5–2.7m) across the west shore of Connecticut, USA, and between 10 and 15ft (3–4.5m) from the New London area eastward. Entire coastal communities were nearly wiped out in New London, Groton and Mystic in Connecticut, as well as from Westerly to Narragansett in Rhode Island (Vallee and Dion, 1998). In September 1975, a storm surge was dramatically captured on camera as Hurricane Eloise struck the Florida panhandle. Eloise began life west of the Leeward Islands, slowly but steadily gaining in strength. As she passed north of Puerto Rico she made landfall on Hispaniola as a weak hurricane, producing widespread flooding and landslides on the island. Eloise crossed the north-west Caribbean and made brief landfall in Mexico near Cancún before turning north and making landfall in Florida with sustained winds of 125mph (109 knots), and gusts of up to 156mph (135 knots). The 10 to 16ft (3–5m) surges of water flooded the shoreline and caused severe erosion, particularly along Walton and Bay counties, with property damage to the value of some $1 billion as more than 8,000 people suffered heavy losses and 500 small businesses were destroyed. Tragically, there were some eighty deaths – four in Florida and the remainder around the Caribbean.

TSUNAMI DANGERS

Of all the coastal forms of inundation, the tsunami is the most feared. The term 'tsunami' comes from the Japanese language, meaning 'harbour wave', and should not be confused with tidal waves. A tsunami is a very large ocean wave caused by an underwater earthquake, landslide or volcanic eruption and can produce the most disastrous coastal flooding, particularly on low-lying coastlines. When a series of tsunami waves approaches a coastline, the first indication is often a sharp swell, not unlike an ordinary storm swell, followed by a sudden outrush of water that often exposes offshore areas as the first wave trough reaches the coast. After several minutes, the first wave strikes, inundating the coast and rushing inland.

In 1755 an earthquake near Lisbon, Portugal, generated tsunamis up to 65ft (20m) high (in some places the waves were reported to have crested at more than 100ft, or 30m), which reached the coasts of Portugal and North Africa, causing large loss of life estimated at around 100,000 people. The tsunami, with less intensity, made it to the coasts of France, Great Britain and Ireland. In Madeira and in the Azores, damage was extensive and many ships were wrecked and lives lost. In 1792, the collapse of part of the Unzen volcano complex on Kyushu Island, Japan, generated a landslide that swept through Shimabara city and straight into the Ariake Sea. The displacement of water triggered a tsunami along the adjacent shoreline of Shimabara peninsula and also across the Ariake Sea into neighbouring provinces. The landslide and tsunami killed around 15,000 people, the worst volcanic disaster in Japan's history (Miyachi, 1992). When the Indonesian volcano of Krakatau blew apart in 1883, it generated a wave that killed 36,000 inhabitants of Java and Sumatra in the Sunda Straits. It was reported that waves were so powerful that coral blocks weighing as much as 600 tonnes were thrown ashore (Francis, 1992). More recently, tsunami flooding received much international attention after the Sumatra-Andaman earthquake in December 2004 which triggered a series of devastating tsunami waves. These hit the coasts of Indonesia, Sri Lanka, South India and Thailand, to name but a few locations, with great violence. The tsunami wave was thought to be around 30ft (9m) high as it approached the shorelines, although in some parts of Indonesia it was reported to have been 65ft (20m). Tragically it killed approximately 200,000 people, although the exact death toll will never be known.

A LONG HISTORY

If there is one thing that evolution has taught us, it is that we cannot live with or without water. Considered as one of the main gifts from the gods, it has supported and destroyed life as we know it, shaped continents and countries, and produced the varied landscape we enjoy today. In times of both flood and drought, many have perished, and the waters of the earth have brought both terror and joy. The influence and impact of, and our association with, water have been probably the most documented out of all the four elements. As one reads shocking historical accounts of some of the most devastating flooding to have affected land and society, these will naturally be compared to events within living memory, and similarities will be drawn. Such comparison and perspective is important, especially when trying to keep an open mind as to future vulnerability under a changing climate.

The United Kingdom and Europe have one of the longest documented histories of flooding in the world. We know this from the translations of numerous chronicles, diaries and annals, with the Irish Annals (e.g. *Annales Quatuor Magistrorum*, 1826 edn) providing some of the earliest dated evidence (Britton, 1937). Although this early and somewhat legendary evidence was no doubt passed from generation to generation, the accounts do make interesting reading. In 2668 BC there was 'an eruption of Lake Con and Lake Techet'. Lake Techet is known today as Lake O'Gara (Lough Gara). There was a 'poisonous inundation of the sea upon the Kingdom . . . whence seven lakes overflowed . . . and therefore they were designated Lake Cuan' in 2654 BC. Lake Cuan is known today as Strangford Lough, located on Ireland's north-east coast. It was in 1544 BC when the first river floods were mentioned, with Subna, Torannia and Cullan overflowing. This was later followed in 1449 BC by the overflowing of the Flaesc, Man and Labrand. Similar inundations are reported up to 506 BC.

GREAT WRITERS

Actual meteorological data did not start to become available in England until the late seventeenth century. The earliest available rainfall record started in 1677 at Towneley Hall near Burnley, Lancashire. Hydrological records from river (and reservoir) gauges came much later, towards the middle of the nineteenth century, with a more formal network being established around the mid-twentieth century. Therefore, much detective work is needed to interpret the descriptions provided by the various diarists, annalists and chroniclers. Many sources of evidence have been consulted for this text, of which those of the great chroniclers have been very useful and provided fascinating reading. There were many great chroniclers and diarists, including Thomas Wykes, John de Taxter, Hector Boece, Robert Fabyan, Samuel Pepys and John Evelyn – in fact too many to mention in great detail, but a few are certainly worthy of discussion, especially for researchers and readers looking to explore further the quotations and events discussed in this text.

It is well known that the chroniclers generally had little hesitation in transcribing and embodying in their own works the writings of their predecessors; it was indeed held among the monastic annalists to be a perfectly legitimate and, more often than not, a necessary practice. A large portion of what we know today and which is described in this text is reliant on their interpretation and transcribing. Many chroniclers wrote about floods, thunderstorms, hailstorms and lightning. It is common to find such descriptions where fatalities or damage occurred, especially during important events like coronations, invasions, battles, funerals and weddings. It is very difficult to ascertain exactly where the chroniclers obtained their information about flood events. It would seem unlikely from some of the very detailed descriptions that these were pure invention. However, as with all such historical sources that describe meteorological and hydrological events, the facts should be treated with due caution. Some of the events will undoubtedly be attached to legend, folklore and mythology, while others will have been passed down ancestral generations orally, and although we must consider that these may contain some truth, no confidence should be placed in any exact dates assigned to events, for obvious reasons.

Roger of Wendover is regarded as the first of the great chroniclers at St Albans Abbey, Hertfordshire. Roger was a Benedictine monk and best known for his work *Flores Historiarum* (Flowers of History), which extended from the Creation to 1235; he died in 1236. The chronicle was composed of a number of sources, more than likely including the work of John de Cella, who was abbot of St Albans from 1195 to 1214. In the preface, Roger said he selected 'from the books of catholic writers worthy of credit, just as flowers of various colours are gathered from various fields', hence the title. *Flores Historiarum* was edited for the English Historical Society in 1841 by H.O. Coxe in five volumes, beginning with the year AD 447, when Roger for the first time turned directly to the history of Britain. In 1890, the more valuable part of the work (from 1154 to 1235) was published as part of the Rolls Series in three volumes. From the year 1202 it was considered a valuable authority, but the material was reworked and in a sense re-edited with editions by Matthaei Parisiensis.

Matthaei Parisiensis (Matthew Paris) was one of the greatest monastic historians of the thirteenth century. Matthew, like Roger of Wendover, was a Benedictine monk based at St Albans Abbey. His great work, the *Chronica Majora* (Chronicles, 1872–84 edn), covered the period from the Creation until 1259, the year of his death. As a historian, Matthew was one of the best-known English chroniclers. It was thought that he collected a lot of information from the many travellers who stopped at St Albans, but this led to criticisms of his work for the possibility that some of his sources provided rumour and gossip. Generally, his writing was regarded as more readable than any of the monastic scholars before him. As well as being a talented writer, Matthew Paris was a good illustrator, and the margins of his books were often filled with drawings and paintings.

Like those of his predecessors, Raphael Holinshed's (*c.* 1529–80) *The Chronicles of England, Scotlande and Irelande* (Chronicles, 1577 edn) are a very useful source of information, which began with the Noachian flood and contained a very detailed study of the history of the countries titled. Initially published in two volumes (and illustrated in places), the texts contained an enormous amount of information, as Raphael was not the only author and source (indeed, the sources are of varying degrees of trustworthiness). The second edition, published in 1587, was said to contain statements that were

Self-portrait of Matthaei Parisiensis (Matthew Paris), *c.* 1200–59. (*© The British Library, MS Royal 14.C.VII, folio 6r*)

offensive to Queen Elizabeth I and her advisers, and immediately after publication some of the pages were excised by order of the Privy Council. It is interesting to note that Holinshed's chronicles have been sourced and used all around the world, and famously by William Shakespeare.

Dr Thomas Short's work *A General Chronological History of the Air, Weather, Seasons, Meteors, etc.* was published in 1749 in two volumes. It is thought that the preparation of this immense work occupied Short for some fifteen to sixteen years and at the time was the most extensive research of its kind. It lists a number of interesting and indeed extreme events, including great earthquakes in Wales in AD 394, and in Cornwall in AD 424, where there were 'great losses, many killed'. In theory, the word 'allegedly' should be used here, as unfortunately Short's work rarely cited an authority or source for his chronology of events, and therefore it is difficult to establish where these were originally recorded, and by whom. Considering the time, research and writing that went into these two substantial volumes, this seems a great pity and one wonders how much of it was indeed factual.

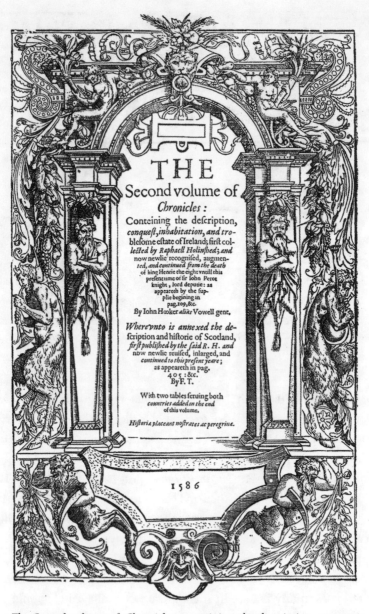

The Second volume of Chronicles: conteining the description, conquest, inhabitation and troublesome estate of Ireland by Raphael Holinshed, from *The Chronicles of England, Scotland and Ireland, London,* printed by Henry Denham, 1586. *(Courtesy Horace Howard Furness Memorial (Shakespeare) Library. © The Schoenberg Center for Electronic Text and Image, University of Pennsylvania Library)*

In 1928, C.E.P. Brooks and J. Glasspoole published *British Floods and Droughts*, in which they rightly question the reliability of some of the early sources: 'It is very difficult to form an opinion as to the amount of credence which should be placed in the sensational reports of the early chroniclers.' But they also admit that many of the historical flood events are so striking that they are definitely worth in-depth discussion. Brooks and Glasspoole considered that the only detailed and reliable weather journal from the Middle Ages was that kept by the Revd William Merle at Oxford between 1337 and 1344, and it is fascinating to read their critique of it: '[The diary] presents a picture which is extraordinarily like that given by day-to-day records of recent years. The winters, sometimes mild and open, sometimes broken by short spells of frost; the summers with a few days of moderate rain alternating with short intervals of golden weather; nothing to remind us that we are reading of the fourteenth century.' The two authors thought more positively about early flood sources and occasionally suggested some justification for events, for example with regard to the Thames flood of AD 9. They pondered how this could have been remembered, but speculate that it may have been possible from news that crossed the Channel to Gaul and then made it to Roman ears.

Very useful, well-documented historical flood information is found in the compilation and corroboration provided by C.E. Britton (1937) in his report to the then Meteorological Office Air Ministry, *A Meteorological Chronology to AD 1450*. This chronology mentioned not only floods but a whole multitude of environmental conditions, including auroras, cold winters, drought, frosts, heavy rainfall, thick snow, hot summers, lightning, severe gales, thunderstorms, tornadoes and wet seasons, to name a few. It is an invaluable resource and source of information and it is a pleasure to highlight some of Britton's reporting within this text. But it was Britton who wrote strong words regarding the chronology of events published by Dr Short: 'In the results he gives us a vast compilation of events without any clue as to where and by whom the majority of them were recorded. Still more remarkable, there are numerous events mentioned, especially those purporting to happen in the first 1,000 years of the Christian era, which appear to have no foundation whatever in fact. Frosts, floods, droughts, storms and other phenomena appear of which it seems impossible to find any mention in the history until they appear in Dr. Short's treatise.'

The fact that Short's work is poorly sourced does not necessarily mean that it should be disregarded or that it lacks potential. In fact, many of the events that he quoted have been corroborated and it would seem very unlikely that he set out intentionally to misreport events; although it is possible that inaccuracy or distortion may have entered aspects of his work, no writer or chronicler is infallible. This text does discuss some of Short's suggested inundation and flood events, on the grounds of human interest. Nevertheless, it should be noted that appropriate caution is needed when considering any unsubstantiated events. Therefore, it is no surprise that Britton (1937) pertinently wrote, 'For a chronology to have its maximum value the attention of the compiler must be directed to two main points – dates and authorities.' It was here that Britton's work came into its own, as his chronology paid careful attention to the citation of authorities. He provided not only a valuable and highly interesting chronology of weather-related events, but also a suitable discussion of any alternative dating given by the original writer, chronicler or annalist. His decision to end his text with events in the year 1450 was based on the premise that it was an era that saw the invention of printing and the beginning of an expansion in sources.

Even by the eleventh century, sources of information on flood events became far more detailed, largely because of the number of chroniclers both at home and abroad. But the interpretations of these events are tricky, as it is often difficult to distinguish the British ones from the foreign, especially those written by continental historians which were then drawn on by British writers. For example, Britton (1937) is quick to point out that, as a result, many droughts in Dr Symons' list in *British Rainfall* (HMSO 1887) did not appear to relate to British events at all.

No discussion of sources would be complete without consideration of the works of eminent meteorologist and climatologist Hubert H. Lamb (1913–97). His contribution towards establishing climate change as a scientific issue of global concern was profound. Of all the texts examined, Lamb's substantial double volume *Climate: Present, Past and Future* (1977), is essential, informative and enjoyable reading. His analysis and catalogue of sea floods, particularly along the North Sea coasts, *Historic Storms of the North Sea, British Isles and Northwest Europe* (1991), is an essential reference for any researcher wishing to examine coastal inundations in detail. Similarly, John Brazell completed a very thorough assessment of *London Weather* that was published by the UK Meteorological Office (HMSO, 1968). Much time and research was devoted by Brazell to analysing the weather and climate of the city and also elements of flooding from the River Thames and Thames estuary. In this work he stated that flooding of the Thames in and around London was often due to a combination of high tide, a tidal surge and a river swollen by heavy or prolonged rain or thawing snow. However, in the assessment of historic flood events it is often difficult to decide which of these factors is specifically responsible. Today we have the luxury of heightened technology, with greater awareness of extended and further sources, and more detailed analysis and corroboration allows a better assessment of these important and valuable accounts. It is therefore the task of the writer to report these as accurately and in as informed a way as possible; it is then up to the reader to decide whether he or she believes the accounts or not.

Population bias, translation and exaggeration are a few vital source considerations when examining historical accounts of flooding, especially those sourcing fatality figures. These figures should be treated with extreme caution. It must be acknowledged that flooding does result in large losses of life. Contemporary events have certainly shown this sadly to be the case. Therefore, single events can result in a death toll into the hundreds of thousands. But most historical accounts are presented as very rough estimates; indeed the figures presented are often rounded to the nearest thousand for extreme events, and such large figures are often designed purely to signify a generally high number of fatalities (sometimes including livestock). These are not exact numbers and it is possible that as the stories were passed through generations the figure may also have altered somewhat.

The descriptive language was also unconventional, with many words conveying a somewhat different meaning; for example, during the thirteenth century the word 'erthequake' (earthquake) was often used to describe thunder. Reports, diaries and journals in the seventeenth and eighteenth centuries which note 'a great flood' often meant a flood that had been caused from a general bank overflow or the natural inundation of floodplains, and therefore not so great in today's terms. The word 'waterspout' is frequently used. This did not always refer to the phenomenon known today as a waterspout at sea or over inland waters, but instead a localised downburst associated with thunderstorms and resembling a dense, dark shaft of rain, essentially a cloudburst.

DATE DEBATE

As with any chronological discussion of flood events that go back centuries, there will be complications. Sometimes the same event is reported in different years by different chroniclers. Sometimes the exact year, month or date is not reported at all. Some sources, such as Lamb (1977), converted all dates to the new-style calendar for a consistent approach; some make no mention of whether the new or old style convention was being used at all, and some medieval writers were known to have constructed their own dating style. Sometimes the date of reporting is interpreted as the actual date of the event. Dates provide a minefield of complexity, and therefore much corroboration is often needed and the sources should naturally be assessed with appropriate caution, especially with regard to the changes in calendar.

The Julian calendar was introduced by Julius Caesar in 46 BC, taking force in 45 BC, with the calendar being generally used in Europe until 1582. The last day of the Julian calendar was 4 October 1582 and this was followed by the first day of the Gregorian calendar, 15 October 1582. Nevertheless, 5 October 1582 to 14 October 1582 (inclusive) are still valid, because most countries did not adopt the new calendar on the date specified. In Britain, the Gregorian calendar was not adopted until 1752, with the introduction of the new calendar on the day following 2 September of that year, which was called 14 September 1752. The loss of eleven days is seen to cause problems in a number of sources.

The discussion of the events in the following chapters examines the diaries, chronicles and annals transcriptions along with press descriptions of many sources of evidence. Dates are given as accurately as possible but it is very clear that many writers over the centuries have struggled to translate between old- and new-style dates. In Britain, and countries of the British Empire, old-style dates mean that the date is within the Julian calendar that was in use in those countries until 1752. The new-style date means that the date is in the Gregorian calendar, adopted on 14 September 1752. In general, most dates discussed from around the middle of the eighteenth century relate to the new-style calendar convention, although there will naturally be some crossover as the date change was not strictly implemented by many of the sources.

AN ACT OF GOD

Before the nineteenth century there was no real scientific way of measuring floods; such analysis and interpretation was based on the devastation produced, and the impression made on the people who experienced them. Medieval chroniclers compared flood events with biblical precedents and the most important flood information was overshadowed by post-flood reporting of the 'wickedness of men' and 'portents of things to come'.

The causes of floods were, and in some cultures and faiths still are, regarded as a punishment from the gods for noise, wickedness, evilness and overpopulation. In other words, the extremities of flooding are often considered an 'act of God', a term that makes many natural disaster experts feel uncomfortable. This expression is still widely used today in reference to extreme events, occasionally with regard to insurance or liability in an effort to define or defend a natural catastrophe. But the contemporary concept and usage of the term are very controversial subjects. One of the reasons for this is that such terminology is poorly defined and therefore loosely used, and occasionally abused. For example, in late 2004 press reports suggested that a number of people who suffered losses, particularly concerning motor vehicles, during the August 2004 flash flood at Boscastle, Cornwall, UK, struggled to get due compensation, as some insurance companies claimed that the floods were an 'act of God' and therefore were not eligible for insurance compensation. Such policy does vary from insurer to insurer, and public and media pressure often helps the claimants' cause. However, closer examination of one glossary of terms relating to car insurance did highlight the following: 'An act of God: An event, which is not the fault of any individual. Acts of God may or may not be insurable.' The 'may' or 'may not' are the key words here.

Similarly, during the floods of January 2005 in Carlisle, Cumbria, UK, one press account read, 'Thousands of customers who lost their telephone service because of Cumbria's storms and floods will not get a penny in compensation.' It was claimed that the damage caused to networks, lines and services was an 'act of God' and therefore uninsurable. It is clear that the term is still being widely used in a number of contexts. If we look at a selection of the many definitions, the problems associated with its understanding and usage become evident:

A sudden and violent act of nature which could not have been foreseen or prevented.

An event arising out of natural causes with no human intervention, which could not have been prevented by reasonable care or foresight; examples are floods, lightning and earthquakes.

An unpreventable and unpredictable event that could cause loss or damage to buildings, land, vehicles etc.

A manifestation especially of a violent or destructive natural force, such as a lightning strike or an earthquake, which is beyond human power to cause, prevent or control.

An extraordinary natural event (as a flood or earthquake) that cannot be reasonably foreseen or prevented; *force majeure*, an inevitable and unavoidable accident.

It is interesting to note that the *Columbia Encyclopaedia* (Lagassé, *et al.* 2000) goes as far as to suggest that an act of God implies no right to damages: 'An act of God, however, is so extraordinary and devoid of human agency that reasonable care would not avoid the consequences; hence, the injured party has no right to damages. Accidents caused by tornadoes, perils of the sea, extraordinary floods, and severe ice storms are usually considered acts of God, but fires are not so considered unless they are caused by lightning.' *The People's Law Dictionary* (Hill and Hill, 2002) suggested that acts of God are significant for two reasons: 'Firstly for the havoc and damage they wreak, and secondly because often contracts state that "acts of God" are an excuse for delay or failure to fulfil a commitment or to complete a project.'

Therefore, acts of God have legal significance especially if the concept is used as a defence against absolute liability in relation to extreme events. Tyrrell

(1999) aptly suggested that it is a term that is used as an initial defence, part of a knee-jerk reaction to claims or fear of liability, and also to sensationalise the weather; therefore headline journalism finds it irresistible. The headlines after the tsunami in south-east Asia in late December 2004 suggested that most travel insurance companies disregarded the act of God exclusion clause after the extreme flood and honoured claims made by travellers caught up in the devastation; but heightened media exposure also helped the plight of victims. It would be fair to say that the majority of insurance companies have modified their policies to include 'all risks', therefore omitting the act of God clause; but certain vulnerable geographical locations are often associated with specific risk, for example flood-prone areas. Maybe the time has come to redefine an 'act of God'? Perhaps there should be less emphasis on religion, and on blame directly attributed to God? Should God be taken out of the equation and no longer used as a defence? Would this be too complex and controversial? Would an 'act of nature' or even 'accident of nature' be more appropriate in today's changing climate? Or perhaps this would only transfer blame from God to nature and open up a whole new avenue of debate? This argument still creates more discussion and questions than it does answers. One thing is for sure: 'acts of God' have been well documented for centuries and this phrase will no doubt be used well into the future during the justification process of extreme flood events that result in the large loss of life.

When one thinks of a specific act of God in connection with flooding, the great Noachian flood is the classic. This is the most discussed and disseminated event of them all, considering that the Bible has been translated into over 2,000 languages, with countless partial and audio translations. The date of the flood is often quoted at around 2448–2345 BC. The dating of the event, along with the fact that there never was any biblical flood that destroyed everyone in the world except for a chosen few, has long been debated. However, we know that such an event exists in the folklore of many cultures, for example the *Epic of Atrahasis* and the Mesopotamian *Epic of Gilgamesh*. The Gilgamesh flood focuses on the character Utnapishtim, a parallel figure and story to that of Noah and the Flood, most probably dating to the third millennium BC.

It was perceived that the early floods were the result of the wickedness, evil, wrong-doing and even noise of mankind, prompting the decision of God that punishment must come as a deluge from the heavens. The book of Genesis tells the story of Noah and the Flood:

> And the waters prevailed,
> and were increased greatly upon the earth;
> and the ark went upon the face of the waters.
> And the waters prevailed exceedingly upon the earth;
> and all the high hills, that were under the whole heaven,
> were covered.
> Fifteen cubits upwards did the waters prevail;
> and the mountains were covered.
> And all flesh died that moved upon the earth,
> both of fowl, and of cattle, and of beast,
> and of every creeping thing that creepeth upon the earth,
> and every man.
>
> *(Genesis 7: 18–21)*

The contemporary text *Before the Flood* (Wilson, 2001) provided an in-depth and fascinating discussion of events. It suggested that the idea of a world flood is undeniably so deeply ingrained in the folk memories of so many different cultures that it raises the fundamental question of just how and why this should be so. In fact, there may be no real mystery, as the answer to this question could be summed up in the six words, 'the end of the Ice Age': 'as has been scientifically established for over a century, the world has repeatedly suffered from Ice Ages, at the last count no less than thirty-six of these occurring during the last three million years.' Climatic changes have caused sea levels to rise and fall many times in the history of the earth. Simply, a cooling trend and times of maximum glaciation can result in large volumes of water being stored, leading to a worldwide fall in sea level. Any warming trend will undoubtedly contribute to melting and subsequent shrinking of ice, leading to sea-level rises. The melting of extensive ice-sheets raises sea levels and therefore global flood vulnerability is increased. Indeed, ice-sheets breaking off from the polar ice-caps could trigger tsunami-sized waves as they slump into the sea. However, it should also be remembered that warming and associated ice-melt is a gradual

The Noachian deluge. (© *Chris Chatfield*)

process and maybe the 'sudden' biblical deluge is in fact the greatest act of God of them all?

Historical accounts of flooding describe, often colourfully, the magnitude and severity of what our ancestors experienced. As with any historical flood report, attention should be paid to dates and authorities in assessing reliability, but it is the descriptions and often detailed information that these authorities provide that aid our knowledge and understanding. Moreover, it is this knowledge and understanding that has helped to save lives. It should be remembered in any discussion of historical flood vulnerability that, particularly over many centuries, differing degrees of protection would have been afforded. Through the costly direct experience of flooding, sufficient knowledge would have been gained to deter settlement in highly vulnerable areas that afforded little or no protection. In time, a better standard of protection would have been developed, and towards the present day, forecasting, warning and dissemination of flood risk are particularly heightened.

The following chapters present a brief chronology, by century, of some of the notable flood events to have taken place in and around the United Kingdom and northern Europe, with some discussion of, and reference to, events further afield. This chronology is not intended to be a definitive catalogue or relative frequency of events. This would be impossible in one text and would require countless volumes to complete. But it provides some very valuable discussion, new information, important comparisons and, above all, perspective during periods of climatic change. Personal perspectives on extreme floods are limited to our short memories or the stories and tales of our close ancestors, but the way we think about extreme flood events is an important part of our understanding of such severe natural disasters as they occur in our lifetime. With weather cycles, natural variability and climatic changes, the future will always possess a high degree of uncertainty; therefore one way to understand future flood vulnerability is to gain a good understanding of past flood climates. But what do we really know about extreme floods of the past?

Chapter 1

FROM THE FIRST TO THE TENTH CENTURY

Thou hast set a bound that they may not pass over; that they turn not again to cover the earth.

(Psalm 104: 9)

ources that refer to the first century provide little detail of the causes and locations affected by flooding in the United Kingdom. This is because the majority of early sources were Roman in origin and although the first official Roman presence in Britain was that of Julius Caesar in 55–54 BC, the Romans did not invade Britain until AD 43, when Emperor Claudius set about dealing with troublesome tribal princes and druids. Some early accounts refer to rainfall; for example, Dr Thomas Short (1749) described 'a rain of blood in London lasting five hours' which occurred in AD 4. Obviously it did not rain actual blood and this description most probably referred to rain mixed with volcanic dust or fine desert sand which had been transported in the atmosphere. Britton (1937) projected much doubt on pre-Roman sources, and his concerns are valid. He suggested that prior to the Roman invasion any reporting of events should be considered 'legendary'. Therefore, such evidence is based on oral tradition which inevitably leads to elements of exaggeration or distortion of the truth.

With all this said, one of the first notable flood events is thought to have occurred in AD 7 (AD 9 in some sources, or possibly there were two separate events) where extensive floods along the River Thames and Thames estuary

31

were described as causing 'heavy casualties'. This also indicated that there was some moderate settlement along the banks and on the floodplain at this time. This early event could have been the result of a storm surge, as reports of flooding were also noted further along the east coast and around the Humber estuary. More specific localities were soon named by Short. In AD 14 the west Midlands suffered 'inundations of the Severn with great damage' and there was a 'great flood' in the Trent Valley in AD 29. A river flood along the Dee in AD 33 caused much damage at Chester, and similar reports are noted in AD 37 with flooding in the Medway, Kent.

ROMAN INVASION

The Annals of Tacitus (1980 edn, p. 363) recorded how two Roman legions under the command of Publius Vitellius marched from the River Ems to the Rhine along the shores of the North Sea in AD 15 when:

> Before long . . . a northerly gale, aggravated by the equinox, during which the Ocean is always at its wildest, began to play havoc with the column. Then the whole land became a flood; sea, shore, and plain were a single aspect. . . . The companies became intermingled, the men standing one moment up to the breast, another up to the chin, in water; then the ground would fail beneath them, and they were scattered or submerged. . . . Words and mutual encouragement availed nothing against the deluge; there was no difference between bravery and cowardice, wisdom and folly, circumspection or chance; everything was involved in the same fury of the elements. Many men were drowned; the survivors reached rising ground, and day brought back the land.

Rivers played an important role during the Roman settlement period and their influence provided further detailed recording of flood events. They were regarded as defence barriers and often formed the boundaries between early kingdoms (later shires). In this context, rivers are mentioned in the conquering of parts of northern Britain by Ostorius Scapula, the second governor of Roman Britain (AD 47–52). Ostorius Scapula conquered the heartland between the rivers Severn and the Trent. For centuries the rivers

Trent and Humber formed the border between England and Scotland. There was immense fluctuation in this border, and in time it eventually settled on the River Tweed. The River Severn is mentioned in AD 14 because it, too, was an important border – between England and Wales. Similarly, the upper Thames was considered the effective border between Mercia and Wessex.

The Thames (and Thames Valley) was the subject of one of the first significant reports specifically detailing flood-related casualties in Britain in AD 48, with casualties estimated (although most probably exaggerated) at 10,000. Brooks and Glasspoole (1928) suggested that this flood may have been due to very high rainfall, but this seems dubious for such a high fatality figure. Clearly the figure is estimated and is likely to include both humans and livestock, but the flood also affected a large portion of the east coast and Thames estuary and it is more than likely the combined result of storm-related rains and tides.

Short suggested that twenty years later an extreme flood changed the landscape of Britain forever. In AD 68, inundations on the south coast apparently separated the Isle of Wight from Hampshire, changing the coastline configuration dramatically. Very little is known about this event, which is speculated to be either flood- or earthquake-related. If flood-related, this would surely have been one of the most notable flood events of the first century in England, if not for many centuries to come. There is no indication as to where Short (1749) obtained such an incredible account and the theory should therefore be noted with interest, but treated as conjecture.

Later, in AD 80, floods along the River Severn cost the lives of many cattle and in AD 95 extensive floods in the Humber estuary resulted in 50 miles of land being inundated. A deluge of heavy rain that lasted for what was said to be an 'incredible nine months' in AD 107 resulted in the corn being washed out of the ground. These long periods of heavy rain and associated crop damage inevitably led to widespread famine and further casualties.

Short (1749) recorded that there were floods along the River Severn in AD 115; Luckombe (1800) noted that similar events occurred around the Humber in AD 125. Marine inundations along the south cost of Dorset in AD 131 were also catalogued in Short, as was the overflowing of the River Trent for 20 miles on each side in AD 218. Large-scale loss of life was reported as a result of floods along the Tweed, also in 218. Flood events continued to be reported through the rest of the third century along the Humber, Tweed, Severn and Dee, with inundations in Thanet, Lancashire, Cheshire and along the Northumberland coast to name but a few. Despite date and source ambiguities, the naming of flood-prone locations does give a good indication of early vulnerability in England.

In Cheshire, a lowland county in north-west England, an estimated 5,000 people and 'innumerable quantity of cattle' were reported drowned in 353. It is very difficult to speculate exactly where in the county such a large number of people would have been lost, but locations in and around Chester and the River Dee could be suggested, as Roman settlement by this time was well established and the Dee already had a long association with flooding.

The Anglo-Saxon period was under way by the middle of the fifth century and London entered the flood history books with a Thames flood 'exceeding 10 miles above and 10 miles below' the capital in 479. Cardiganshire, a west-coast county of Wales bordering the Irish Sea, was subjected to a storm surge in Cardigan Bay in 520. There were further inundations in the Humber (529) and Tweed (536), which resulted in heavy casualties. AD 564 was noted as a year of 'great rain floods'. East Anglia received a coastal deluge in 575, with similar inundations at Anglesea (Anglesey), an island county of north-west Wales, in 580. There were floods around the North Sea during May 586, and then on the north-east coast in 589 affecting Hartlepool. There is some obvious disharmony between writers and chroniclers regarding the Hartlepool event. Seller, in his text *The History of England* (1696), mentioned flooding as follows: 'And the sea breaking in near Hortle Pool [Hartlepool] in the Bishoprick of Durham swept away divers villages, drowning many people and cattle.' But Britton (1937) suggested that this event was probably quite mythical. This may be a presumptuous suggestion by Britton based on his opinion of sourcing by Seller. However, such coastal and fluvial flooding (the River Tees and its tributaries have a long history of overflowing) in and around Hartlepool during this year should not be considered implausible.

FLOOD ATTACK

By the seventh century, London was under flood attack from the Thames (in 630) and it was Scotland which featured prominently in reports in the

700s, when inundations at Edinburgh did great damage in 730. Dr Thomas Short (1749) reported that some 400 families were drowned at Glasgow in 738. The ninth and tenth centuries brought more detailed reporting and interpretation of flood events but these were cold centuries, notable for frozen rivers rather than flooded ones. This did not stop the assaults of south-westerly weather systems which generated a windstorm and flood on 23–4 December 800.

Britton (1937, p. 29) quoted the translated works of Simeon of Durham, who described a great wind that 'by its indescribable violence destroyed and threw to the ground cities, many houses and numerous villas, innumerable trees also were torn up by the roots and thrown to the earth. An inundation of the sea burst beyond its bounds not fulfilling what the psalms say, "Thou has set them their bounds which they shall not pass."' This resulted in the deaths of many cattle in England, and across the Channel much of Heligoland was lost, with a high number of fatalities.

Heligoland has a very interesting history and what appeared to be a storm surge in December 800 certainly contributed to this. It is located some 43 miles (70km) from the German coastline and today consists of two islands, which were connected until 1720 when the natural connection was destroyed by yet another storm surge. The original formation itself goes back to the early Eocene geological age, and is considered somewhat of an oddity as the main island's characteristic red sedimentary rock is unusual in the middle of the German Bight. It is not known to form cliffs anywhere else along the North Sea coast, but the bedrock of white chalk is the same as that which forms the white cliffs of Dover and cliffs of other Danish and German islands in the Baltic Sea. A small chalk rock close to Heligoland, called the 'Whitte Klippe' (White Cliff), is known to have existed within sight of the island until the eighteenth century, but heavy seas finally eroded it to below sea level.

In 697, Radbod, the Frisian king, retreated to the then single island after his defeat by the Franks. Over the centuries the island changed ownership and was the subject of many a battle, with the most famous being the naval Battle of Heligoland Bight during the First World War on 28 August 1914. The floods of 800 not only left their mark on Heligoland but extended to the Dutch coast, indicating what must have been a severe North Sea storm surge. Similar inundations were to follow in 864 affecting the Humber and again down into the Netherlands.

During the tenth century, attention is drawn to Ireland, where in 920 (some sources suggest 918), flood waters reached the Abbey of Clonmacnoise and to the Road of the Three Crosses in Ulster. Clonmacnoise, in Offaly County, Ireland, suffered again in 942 when another great flood was said to have completely demolished the eastern part of the settlement, which flanked the side of the River Shannon, in a shallow valley close to the floodplain. St Ciaran, the son of an Ulsterman who had settled in Connaught, chose the site of Clonmacnoise in 545 because of its 'ideal location' at the junction of the river. This was the start of a long association of suffering and survival in vulnerable inhabited locations around the United Kingdom and Ireland.

Chapter 2

THE ELEVENTH CENTURY

. . . the sea overflowed its banks in Kent, and lay'd under water all the lands that had been Earl Goodwin's.

(John Seller)

There were a number of very long, cold, severe winters this century. Early records suggested a severe frost in Ireland lasting some three months between January and March 1008. An English Channel gale wrecked ships and took many lives off Sandwich, Kent, in 1008. Britton (1937, p. 39) discussed the marine flooding of September 1014 as reported in *The Anglo-Saxon Chronicle*: 'On St. Michael's mass eve, came the great sea flood widely through this country, and ran so far up as it never before had done, and drowned many vils [villages], and of mankind a countless number.'

These could be the same floods mentioned by the Scottish historian Hector Boece, whose Latin history of Scotland was translated in around 1531 into Scots prose by John Bellenden, and in 1535 into a verse chronicle, *The Buik of the Croniclis of Scotland* (Stewart, 1858): 'The sea, in the simer, rais forther on the land, than evir it was sene afore in ony time.'

The sea not only flooded the coasts of England but also had devastating consequences to Walcheren (an island in Zeeland province, Netherlands, in the estuary of the River Schelde) and Flanders, including the low-lying borders of northern France. It is also interesting to note that this year was known for an atmospheric calamity when a 'heap of cloud fell and smothered thousands'. This description clearly contains some colourful distortion for what was conceivably a flash flood event as a result of a heavy rainstorm and cloudburst.

Great inundations were also reported along the River Severn in 1046, which were responsible for cattle fatalities. A very wet year in Ireland in 1050 produced a flash flood in which there was damage to buildings and property, with 'milk, fruit and fish' carried away, although no exact locations are mentioned in the sources. In 1076, a heavy rainfall and flash flood in Lincolnshire was described by Abbot Ingulphus in *The Chronicle of the Abbey of Croyland* (1908 edn, p. 155) with a poignant reference to biblical times, 'when, behold! A most dense cloud covered the sun in his course, and brought on, as it were, the shades of night, while the heavens poured forth such a deluge of rain, that, from the flowing of the waters, the days of Noah were thought to have come again.'

Records in *The Anglo-Saxon Chronicle* (Chronicles, 1861 edn, p. 187) described 1086, the year in which Domesday Book was completed in England, as a 'very heavy and toilsome and sorrowful year in England, through murrain of cattle, corn and fruits were at a stand, and so great unpropitiousness in weather as no one can easily think'. The weather at the time was characterised by thunder and lightning which 'killed many men', presumably struck by lightning as opposed to falling victim to any flooding; however, the conditions did lead to localised heavy rains and flash floods and there were reports of great inundations which caused losses in many places when 'rocks were loosened and overwhelmed several towns in their fall'. This echoes memories of twentieth-century floods at Lynton and Lynmouth in Devon, where the flood waters carried large rocks and damaging debris in their wake to seal the fate of the village and ultimately cost many lives. The loss of life from these thunderstorms was paralleled in 1087, when accounts referred to the post-storm famine and diseases that ensued. *The Anglo-Saxon Chronicle* (1861 edn, p. 187) noted:

Such a malady fell on men that almost every other man was in the worst evil, that is with fever, and that so strongly that many men died of the evil. Afterwards there came, through the great tempests which came as we have told before [1086], a very great famine all over England, so that many hundred men perished by death through famine.

Heavy rains and swollen rivers influenced the demise of Scottish King Malcolm III in 1093. King Malcolm III travelled south into Northumberland,

38

seeking vengeance for treatment at the court of King William Rufus (forcing him to pay homage in 1091 and then seizing the border city of Carlisle and the region of Cumbria in 1092). His huge army encamped just north of Alnwick and it was here that Robert de Mowbray, governor of Bamburgh Castle, rode out with a small contingent to repel them. Mowbray managed a surprise attack on the Scots that threw them into complete confusion, but a sudden deluge of rain and the floods that resulted were another surprise for Malcolm, whose 'army either fell by the sword, or those who escaped the sword were carried away by the inundations of the rivers, which were more than usually swollen by the winter rains' (Britton, 1937, p. 49). The floods in the valleys prevented their retreat and King Malcolm was slain in the battle and his army defeated.

GOODWIN SANDS

The south-east coast of England was subjected to a notable storm surge in November 1099, in which a sea flood sprang up to such a degree and did so much harm as 'no man remembered that it ever before did'. This storm surge affected not only the coast of Kent and the Thames estuary, but it pushed down the North Sea towards the Netherlands with tragic consequences. In total, some 100,000 people were estimated (possibly overestimated) to have drowned from this event, in what can only have been the most terrifying inundation of water to the inhabited coastal lowlands.

The east coast of Kent took a fair share of the storm surge and legend has it that this 1099 coastal storm was responsible for the formation of the infamous Goodwin Sands. The sands are a stretch of shoals and sandbars about 10 to 12 miles (16–19km) long and 5 miles (8km) across at their widest, which now lie around 4 to 6 miles (6–10km) off Deal on the east coast of Kent. The series of sandbanks was named after the original landowner, Earl Goodwin (or Godwin), the Earl of Wessex and father of King Harold II, who was said to have owned what was then the island of Lomea, encompassing 4,000 acres of fertile but low-lying land with a sea wall all the way around. But the sea wall became neglected and did not last long. John Seller (1696) suggested that many parts of Kent 'lay'd under water' in 1099, including the land that had been Earl

An unsuspecting vessel runs aground on the Goodwin Sands, 1099. (© *Chris Chatfield*)

Goodwin's. As a result, villages were washed away and many people and livestock drowned. Although it was thought that the events of 1099 were responsible for the formation of the sands, which were to become known as the 'shippe-swallower' and 'the widower', events in 1092 and 1097 are also likely to have been highly influential in their creation. In fact, it would be highly plausible that their origins were influenced by a number of successive coastal storms. The great inundation of 1099 would have been a further, highly influential event. The debate on their exact formation will continue, but what is certain is that the sands have been responsible for a large loss of life and shipping, particularly in 1703, when around one-third of the British navy's home fleet crashed on to the sands with the loss of some great warships (it was estimated that as many as thirteen men-o'-war were lost, with over 2,000 lives). Today, the sands constantly change in configuration as a result of the strong winds and tidal currents, making them difficult to chart with accuracy.

Chapter 3

THE TWELFTH CENTURY

> . . . the sea passed over its usual limits, in consequence of which the lands
> on the coast which had been sown with corn were destroyed in many places.
>
> *(Robert de Monte)*

According to *The Anglo-Saxon Chronicle*, 1116 and 1117 were very wet years, with heavy rainfall and localised flooding proving detrimental to the corn and fruit crops. Lamb (1977) noted that in 1125 many villages were destroyed and suggested that this was the result of a great sea flood. This could be an event in its own right or based on events described in *The Anglo-Saxon Chronicle* (Chronicles, 1861 edn), which recorded that the most notable flood was on 10 August: 'On so great a flood on St. Lawrence's mass day that many towns and men were drowned and bridges shattered, and corn and meadows totally destroyed.' Such a devastating summer flood resulted in diseases to both men and cattle and the widespread failure of the fruit crop, leading to famine. It would seem that the floods were flash flood-related, induced by fearsome thunderstorms. *The Chronicle of Peterborough* (Chronicles, 1849 edn) mentioned a severe thunderstorm with damaging hail during the summer of 1125, and this was repeated by Griffiths (1983) in *A Chronology of Thames Floods*, which noted that the summer of 1125 was very wet.

MONARCHY AND FLOODS

The year 1135 saw the death of King Henry I, and a number of writers commented on the weather around this time, particularly during the autumn,

41

which produced a 'terrible tempest' between 27 and 28 October 1135, affecting the European continent, as it was known and shaped at this time. In France, windstorms damaged Normandy, and there was extensive flooding along the coasts of north-west Germany and the Netherlands. The twelfth century was prolific in sea floods, especially in 1145 and 1151; in Ireland, the winter of the latter year was described as very tempestuous, boisterous and portentous, with 'great overflowings of the sea'. A summer flood on 11 August 1156 as a result of persistent heavy rains hindered the gathering of the harvest and the subsequent sowing of seed.

Even Henry II could not fight the heavy rains and flash flooding in Wales during his war campaigns in 1164/5. Between October 1164 and September 1165 Henry II was in Wales three times: at Abergavenny, at Rhuddlan and in the Berwyn mountains. Caradoc of Llancarvan (the suggested writer of the early part of the *Brut y Tywysogion*) is referenced by Britton (1937, p. 64): 'and there the king encamped, with his advanced troops, in the mountains of Berwyn. And after remaining there for a few days, he was overtaken by a dreadful tempest of the sky, and extraordinary torrents of rain.' There is some difficulty over the exact date of the storm but it seems this is also the storm referred to by Giraldus Cambrensis (1602 edn), who suggested that King Henry II, as a result of a sudden and violent fall of rain, was forced to retreat with his army. Giraldus Cambrensis or Gerald de Barri (Gerald the Welshman or Gerald of Barry) was a writer and cleric. He was one of the most intriguing figures in the history of medieval Wales. During his education in Paris, he achieved a superb command of Latin. However, his expectations of succeeding his uncle as bishop in 1176 were quashed, possibly because of his Welsh blood. Despite this rejection, he became chaplain to King Henry II of England in 1184, and was chosen to accompany one of the King's sons, John, on an expedition to Ireland. This, among other things, led to his becoming one of the first writers to describe Irish music. This visit to Ireland was the catalyst for his literary career, his account being published as *Topographia Hibernica*. He followed it up, shortly afterwards, with an account of Henry's conquest of Ireland, the *Expugnatio Hibernica*. It was his earlier texts that described the Welsh flood that influenced the King's retreat. Indeed, it was actually Giraldus' editor who placed this event in 1165. It would seem that this date is plausible, as other sources suggest that it was in August 1165 that Henry's great army

King Henry II's troops retreat from the Berwyn mountains, August 1165. *(© Chris Chatfield)*

marched westwards up the Ceiriog valley towards Corwen on the other side of the Berwyn mountain range. Twentieth-century writers like Gregory (1993) still subscribe to this: 'As the invading army slowly trudged up the Berwyn Mountains, the incessant rain and the buffeting wind helped the darting raids of Welsh guerrilla bands, making life unbearable for Henry's army. Progress became impossible through the mud and moorland bogs, so the Norman army retreated back to England.' Giraldus became a prolific writer and his work reflected experience gained on his travels as well as his knowledge of the authorities on learning, a recipe of success for any budding author.

A TERRIBLE TEMPEST

August 1165 was also unsettled elsewhere, and thunderstorms and heavy rain-falls affected Yorkshire, including, notably, Scarborough. *The Chronicle of Melrose* (Chronicles, 1856b edn, p. 130) described events with interesting symbolism:

43

There was a great tempest in the province of York during that same month [August]. Many people saw the old enemy taking the lead in that tempest: he was in the form of a black horse of large size, and always kept hurrying towards the sea, while he was followed by thunder and lightning, and fearful noises and destructive hail. The footprints of this accursed horse were of a very enormous size, especially on the hill near the town of Scardeburch [Scarborough], from which he gave a leap into the sea; and here for a whole year afterwards, they were plainly visible, the impression of each foot being deeply graven in the earth. The same tempest destroyed a mill on the River Severn, with its inhabitants, with the exception of a single monk.

This was an early description of a tornado in the United Kingdom, and 'the old enemy' was likely a reference to the well-known appellation of the Devil; other tornado accounts described this enemy as 'Old Nick'. The horse (tornado) he was riding left notable 'footprints' or hoof marks (the tornado track). United Kingdom tornado records show an earlier, more severe event on 23 October 1091 in London, which destroyed the church of St Mary-le-Bow and some 600 homes. Four of the church's 26ft-long rafters were reportedly driven so hard into the ground that only 4ft (1.2m) of them was visible. In theory, since this occurrence, there have been some 36,000 tornado events in the United Kingdom. On average, forty tornadoes are reported each year. This average is based on a contemporary thirty-year period, although in reality the actual figures do vary from year to year. Therefore, the events of 1091 and 1165, though extreme, are not such rare occurrences.

DUTCH DEFIANCE

Marine inundations during March 1170 are discussed by Britton (1937, p. 65), who referred to an account by Robert de Monte which detailed an unusual discovery during Lent when 'the sea passed over its usual limits, in consequence of which the lands on the coast which had been sown with corn were destroyed in many places, the sea having swept over them. This washing away of the land exposed to view in England the bones of a giant, whose body is reported to have been 30 feet [9m] long.' Later this year, on 3 November, further coastal inundations occurred along the Dutch coast and as a result much of Borkum was lost.

Another east-coast storm surge was recorded in January 1176 (although sourced as 1177/8 by some chroniclers and writers), affecting a large part of Lincolnshire where the highest walls, built of turfs (peat cut for fuel), were knocked down by the inundation of the sea. In the Netherlands, the devastation was profound as the sea broke through the dykes, 'which of old had been raised against the tempestuous force of the waves', and broke into the low-lying flat land, drowning cattle as well as 'a multitude of men'. The rest of the inhabitants with difficulty survived, by climbing trees and on to rooftops. It was reported that the flood waters took two days to recede.

The Dutch have had a constant battle with the sea for well over 2,000 years and it is no surprise that they are renowned for saying, 'God created the earth; the Netherlanders created the Netherlands.' It is the Friesians (residents of Friesland, whose territory followed the coast of the North Sea from the mouth of the River Rhine up to the Ems) who are regarded as some of the first coastal managers, as they built *terpen*, the first dykes to hold back the sea. Flooding was clearly a major concern to coastal communities by the twelfth century and early simple protection measures were in place to help protect vulnerable areas.

The twelfth century ended with what was dubbed a very wet year. In 1199 there were such 'vast floods of water that bridges, mills and houses were carried away'. The chronicler Roger de Hoveden (Chronicles, 1868–71 edn) described how the bridge at Berwick, Northumberland was carried away by the River Tweed, and the subsequent disputes involved in its rebuilding. Roger de Hoveden was probably a native of Hoveden or, as it is now called, Howden, in Yorkshire. He was certainly an important man, being a king's clerk (*clericus regis*) during the time of Henry II, and attached to the king's court, from where he was despatched on confidential missions. As a chronicler he was considered fairly impartial and accurate and his reporting of environmental events during the twelfth and early thirteenth centuries is fascinating. His chronicle ended rather abruptly in 1201 and it is therefore assumed he died suddenly.

Chapter 4

THE THIRTEENTH CENTURY

. . . a great deluge of rain so that the channels of the air were uncovered to the cataracts and the clouds were seen to pour out upon the earth to destroy it.

(Matthew Paris)

T he thirteenth century started with some very notable descriptions of severe weather. In Ireland, 1200 was a bleak time, described as a 'cold foodless year, the equal of which no man witnessed in that age'. Throughout the British Isles, the year had a fair share of thunderstorms and heavy rain, with one particular storm at Newmarket killing a monk en route to Bury St Edmunds. He was struck by lightning together with his horse, and both died, apparently without any visible wounds. There was particularly inclement weather in November 1200, known from an account of the transition of the body of Bishop Hugh (bishop and founder of Lincoln cathedral) from London to Lincoln, where lighted tapers struggled to remain lit for the four-day journey. Twenty years after his death, Bishop Hugh was canonised by Pope Honorius III to become the first Carthusian saint, St Hugh of Lincoln.

It was the violent thunderstorms in June and July 1201, with their intense summer rains, that caused flash flooding. On 25 June a 'violent tempest of thunder, lightning and hail arose, with deluging rain, by which men, animals and crops were destroyed'. Fifteen days later, on 10 July, another storm arose, not unlike the first, so that meadows could not be cut and 'hay was carried away in the rapid flow of waters.' It was reported that a great number of fish died as a result of the fouling of the flood water due to decomposing hay. Ralph of Coggeshall (Chronicles, 1875 edn), Abbot of Coggeshall Cistercian Abbey (elected 1207–18), wrote, 'Also so great an inundation was projected forth from the clouds, notably in divers neighbouring provinces, that bridges were broken down, crops and hay carried away, some even submerged, and several people were afraid that in this outpouring of waters the deluge of God was seen again'. Other writers referred to these storms, and the Waverley Annals (Annals, 1865 edn) noted that the abbey was deeply flooded. Amazingly, the Margan Annals (Annals, 1864a edn) suggested that it rained continuously from 13 May to 8 September, which seems somewhat exaggerated, but all sources confirm flood damage to agricultural communities. Locations badly affected included those in and around Exeter, Devon, and St Ives, Cornwall.

Frequent thunderstorms continued to be reported in August 1202, but it was the April floods of 1203 that 'suddenly swelled up way beyond normal levels around a number of places in England', but interestingly, 'only small rains preceded so great a flood'. A disastrous and extreme flood occurred in Perth on 9 September 1210, with many casualties, including members of the Scottish nobility. The Queen herself is reported to have had a narrow escape from drowning during this flood event. 'So violent was the torrent that the whole town was undermined, the houses leveled, and many persons of both sexes lost their lives.' Coates (1916) rightly noted there may be some embellishment of picturesque exaggeration in this account, but all the historians agree that the inundation was a very terrible one.

Walter of Coventry was an English monk and chronicler, probably connected with a religious house in York. He is known to us only through the historical compilation which bears his name, the *Memoriale fratris Walteri de Cowntria* (later edited by William Stubbs, 1873). In this it is noted that on 8 September 1214, 'the unusually high flow of the sea tide caused damage in England'. This looks like a North Sea storm surge, the body of water moving so fast and amplified to such an extent that at Brugge in Belgium the sea flowed over 4 miles inland.

November 1218 produced a devastating weather system between the 17th and 29th. Matthew of Westminster (1570 edn) wrote, 'On the night of St. Andrew an incomparable and unprecedented storm with thunder, lightning, wind and rain burst fearfully upon the whole world in both eastern and western parts and the sea suddenly gathered and swelled like the Nile.' Matthew Paris (1872–84 edn) added, 'This tempest was so general that in England and Scotland it engendered unprecedented thunder and lightning.' But it was the 'great floods in the night of winter' on 17 November that produced tragic consequences. The floods affected both the Netherlands and Germany, and it was estimated that some 100,000 lives were lost in the flood waters, probably a result of a North Sea storm surge. As a result of this inundation, it is thought that a new tidal basin, Jadebusen, was formed (near Wilhelmshaven, Germany).

The Annals of Loch Cé (Annals, 1871 edn) declared 1219 a very wet year in Ireland, noting remarkable rain the whole year, except for a few days. The start of 1219 was exceptionally stormy, creating a catastrophic North Sea storm in January which claimed an estimated 36,000 lives along the Friesland coast (west Jutland and Schleswig-Holstein), with acres of land permanently lost to the sea at Nordstrand (on the coast of Schleswig).

Thunderstorm induced flash flooding continued to remain prevalent in the records. In 1222, there was a severe storm on 14 September, followed by what was reported as 'great rains' continuing until 2 February 1223. 'At the exaltation of the holy cross, there was much thunder throughout all England and this was followed by deluges of rain, with whirlwinds and violent gusts, and this tempestuous weather, together with an unseasonable atmosphere, continued until the Purification of St. Mary.' The references here are to key dates in the church calendar and these provide a reasonable guide to the timing of events during the medieval period. The Feast of the Presentation of Christ in the Temple, also known as The Purification of Saint Mary the Virgin, fell on 2 February. These 'deluges of rain' produced widespread damage, especially to farmland and crops. Ravensdale (1974) noted that thirteen arable acres could not be ploughed, 'which were in meadow and pasture because of too much rain'.

The power and intensity of thunderstorms are well reported in the thirteenth century and such descriptions aid our understanding of why short periods of extreme precipitation caused so much flood damage. On 30 November 1222, a severe thunderstorm in Warwickshire destroyed churches and church towers, houses and outbuildings, along with the walls and ramparts of castles. A number of sources mention that two small towers of Worcester cathedral were demolished by this storm, and in the town of Pilardeston in Warwick the storm destroyed the house of a knight, burying his wife and eight other people. This stormy period continued until 12 December, when a 'sudden storm of wind arose, which raged more fiercely than the before mentioned tempest', where it 'threw down buildings as if they were shaken by the breath of the devil, levelled churches and their towers [including Dunstable church and Merton Church] to the ground, tore up the roots of trees of the forest and fruit trees, so that scarcely a single person escaped without suffering loss.' It was also mentioned by Short (1749) that 'inundations due to a very high tide' occurred this year. Given the nature of the driving windstorm towards the end of the year, tidal floods seem very plausible.

This was a prelude to what was a very wet 1223, with many river and flash flood events as a result of prolonged rainfall. Matthew Paris wrote of the 'rain and overflowing of waters continuing in every month of the year that it greatly hindered the seasons and the fruits were very late in maturing, so much so that in the month of November there were hardly any crops to lay up.' Indeed, intense rainfall as a result of a cloudburst was said to 'choke many people'. This could indicate drowning or possibly be a reference to the sulphurous air produced by the thunderstorm. The clear, crisp smell of air after a thunderstorm is the smell of ozone, the charged odour of air. It is theorised that when ozone is charged, creating an unstable element, it becomes highly reactive and sulphur as an odour is smelt. Other theories are more specific and assume that sulphurous air can be produced by two atoms of oxygen being smashed into one atom of sulphur. The debate concerning the exact scientific cause of the smell of sulphur during storms continues, but historical descriptions of this distinct pungent smell have been noted by many writers, for example in *The Odysseys of Homer* (1857 edn) it was written, 'Zeus thundered and hurled his bolt upon the ship, and she quivered from stem to stern, smitten by the bolt of Zeus, and was filled with sulphurous smoke.'

An 'awful and strange shower' in Connaught, Ireland in 1224 led to 'terrible diseases and distempers among cattle that grazed on the land where the shower fell, and their milk produced, in the persons who drank it, extraordinary internal diseases.' In 1227 the Dee Bridge at Chester collapsed during a flood, and the Annals of Worcester (Annals, 1869b edn) noted that the winter of 1227–8 produced serious river floods in December, January and February, such that 'no one then living had ever seen the like in their time.'

SUMMER FLOODS

Heavy summer rainfalls returned to many parts in July 1233 and great floods resulted. Described as 'sudden inundations', the level of flood water was extraordinary in many parts, notably in southern Britain (as mentioned in the Annals of Winchester, 1870 edn). As a result, people and animals drowned, buildings, mills and bridges were irreparably destroyed and irrecoverable damage was done to crops and fruit; famine and disease ensued. One location to report flood damage was the House of Waverley, a monastery near Farnham, Surrey. Steeped in history, the Cistercian monastery was founded on 24 November 1128 by William Giffard, Bishop of Winchester, who brought over from the Abbey of Aumône, in Normandy, twelve brethren with their abbot to form the first colony. The location of the abbey, in the Wey Valley, was not ideal as the monks suffered from periodic flooding and crop failure. During times of severe hardship the community at Waverley was forced to disband and seek asylum in other monasteries, notably in 1203 owing to a bad harvest. But it was on 11 and 12 July 1233 that the Annals of Waverley (Annals, 1865 edn, p. 312) recorded:

> . . . a terrible tempest, violent beyond precedent, raged. Stone bridges and walls were broken down and destroyed, rooms and all the offices were violently tumbled together, and, even at the new monastery, there was flooding in several places to the height of 8 feet. Damage and inconvenience to the same house was such that, in the building in which manifold things both interior and exterior were lost, no one is able or certain to value them.

This is one of the first flash flood events that mention both inundation levels (8ft, or 2.4m) and an initial assessment of economic loss – the monastery was not the wealthiest in the land but clearly their belongings at the time were priceless or irreplaceable, or both.

A repeat of such summer flooding occurred on 16 July 1234 and affected many areas between Bedford and Norfolk: 'There suddenly arose a great storm of thunder, lightnings, and whirlwinds, attended by inundations of rain and hail.' 'Whirlwinds' possibly refers to a tornado recorded at Abbotsley, Cambridgeshire, in July 1234. This storm system had major implications for crops as 'the corn in the fields was lifted up by a blast from hell, the cattle and birds, with everything growing in the fields, were destroyed as if trodden down by carts and horses.' Roger of Wendover described the passage of, and area affected by, this storm in good detail and suggested that it commenced on the boundaries of Bedford, moving east through the Isle of Ely and then Norfolk, before moving out to sea.

LONDON BRIDGE

London and the River Thames soon became a focus of interest during the early thirteenth century as the early timber London Bridge over the River Thames was replaced with a stone version, completed in 1209 after some thirty-three years of construction. The bridge included houses, shops, and even a chapel built at the centre, and illustrations show it crowded with buildings of up to seven storeys high. But the medieval bridge had nineteen small arches, which influenced the passage of water. The apertures between the pillars were fairly narrow and restricted the flow of water through the structure. Effectively, it was holding up the flow of water and the difference in water level each side of the structure was at times around 6ft (1.8m), especially during heavy rainfall.

Brazell (1968) suggested that the bridge blocked a staggering 80 per cent of the river flow, which was obstructed by the addition of water-wheels under the two north arches to drive water pumps, and under the two south arches to provide the power for grain mills. It was no surprise that ferocious rapids were produced between the bridge supports. Only the brave or foolhardy attempted to navigate a boat under the bridge, and in fact many were drowned trying to do so. In 1429 the Duke of Norfolk was thrown into the water, and in 1628 Queen Henrietta also had a close encounter with the rapids. Therefore, it soon became renowned as the bridge 'for wise men to pass over, and for fools to pass under'.

ANNUS HORRIBILIS

It was not long into 1236 that flooding was being well reported, especially when Westminster Palace was entered by a deluge from the River Thames as 'monsoon-like rains poured from leaden skies' during January, February and early March 1236, indicating prolonged heavy rains. As the Thames overflowed, it must have been an incredible sight to see small boats navigating the forecourt of Westminster Palace where residents went to their chambers on horseback. But what followed was one of the driest summers, being described as 'unbelievable' after such torrential spring downpours.

The summer of 1236 produced a lengthy drought with 'an almost intolerable heat which continued for four months or more'. The result of this was that rivers, deep pools and ponds dried up and water mills stood useless and ultimately profitless. With the water resource exhausted, large cracks appeared in the ground and the corn crop in many places grew barely above 2ft (0.6m). The drought ended with heavy October rains, particularly in northern England, which led to flooding, so much so that streams and lakes overflowed, damaging a number of bridges and mills. But worse was to come on 12 November 1236 during a devastating storm surge which coincided with a high tide; there was flooding to low-lying coastal areas and harbours between the Wash and the Thames estuary (as far inland as Woolwich). In one village, north of Wisbech, Cambridgeshire, around 100 people, along with all the sheep and cattle, drowned. This was colourfully described by Matthew Paris (Chronicles, 1872–84 edn, vol. 3, p. 379):

> . . . a wonderful inundation of the sea broke suddenly in the night, and a great wind roared with the seas, and there were great and unusual floods in the rivers which, especially in places near the sea, forced ships from their harbours by dragging their anchors, drowned a multitude of men, destroyed flocks of sheep and herds of cattle, tore trees up by the roots, overturned houses, and ravaged the coast. And it ascended the shores increasingly, flowing for two days and the intervening night, which was unheard of, and it did not flow and ebb in the usual way but was prevented, as people said, by the very great violence of the opposing wind. The corpses of the drowned were seen unburied near the shore, thrown by

Residents near Wisbech, Cambridgeshire, attempting to save themselves from the flood water on 12 November 1236. (© *Chris Chatfield*)

the sea into caves, so that at Wisbech and the neighbouring villages, and along the shore and sea coast, a great number of men perished. Indeed, in one village, not a populous one, over 100 bodies were consigned to the tomb in one day.

The chronicler Raphael Holinshed (Chronicles, 1577 edn) also described how a great tidal surge arrived from the east, 'for several days with unabated fury, washing up the ocean in such tremendous waves that the banks gave way and the whole country lay completely exposed to its awful fury.'

The year ended with notable thunderstorms and flash floods which 'shook towers and buildings' on 23 December. This affected many parts of England, and in Wales it was reported that 'one night before Christmas Eve there arose a remarkable wind to break down an immense number of houses and churches, and to injure the tree and kill many men and animals'. There ends a remarkable year for its extremities of weather and flood waters.

BURST BANKS

Between December 1236 and March 1237 there were 'great rains and floods'. A climax of events occurred in February 1237 in which the River Thames, and the River Seine in France, allegedly created a flood of such proportions that the swollen rivers 'destroyed cities, bridges and mills' and made lakes out of dry land. It may be a slight exaggeration to suggest that cities were destroyed, but this account is based on an inundation period of some eight to fifteen days. Similar floods were repeated a year later and recorded by a number of sources, including Matthew Paris and the Waverley Annals, during the autumn and winter of 1238, when rivers of England 'unaccustomedly and unnaturally burst forth violently upon numerous fields, level ground and dry and waterless places, and increased rapidly to swift torrents so that fish were taken in them'. It is interesting to note that just one year later the floods were still described as 'unaccustomed' and 'unnatural', but without their locations it is difficult to say whether they refer to new places of inundation or indeed refer to flooding in what we know today as a floodplain, an area of land around a river or watercourse which does flood naturally from time to time.

The River Severn continued to flood and created problems at Gloucester in 1240, but this was surpassed by yet another 'huge deluge' in London, in which the River Thames overflowed after a thunderstorm on 19 November 1242 (and conditions continued unsettled until the 27th); there was flooding in the Westminster Hall, where, as in 1236, boats were floated and lawyers were carried into their offices on horseback. Conditions were described by Matthew Paris (Chronicles, 1872–84 edn) as 'continually unsettled weather lasting for many days, and sad disturbance of the air. Deluges of rain fell, so that the river Thames, overflowing its usual banks, caused floods for six miles around Lambeth, and unseasonably took possession of houses and fields there.'

DEMISE OF OLD WINCHELSEA

Without the influence of water, the United Kingdom would not be the shape it is today. It is sometimes hard to visualise the mechanisms which took place in separating the United Kingdom from the continent of Europe at a time when the River Thames was a tributary of the Rhine. The encroachment of water through rises in sea level, erosion by the waves, surges of sea, flash flood waters and the channelling of rivers has played an important part in our geomorphological history. A flood record for AD 68 described how the Isle of Wight became separated from Hampshire during an incredible inundation. This should not be interpreted as fact, but sudden storm surges have shaped the landscape of many counties and decided the fate of towns and villages. The coastal floods and accompanying windstorms of 1 October 1250 produced widespread flooding around the Humber, the Wash and the low-lying North Sea coasts in the south-east. The marine floods in that year also made their way around the south coast to the infamous town of Old Winchelsea, East Sussex (near Rye). Recorded as Winceleseia in 1130 and Old Wynchchelse in 1321, the town and port stood on the shingle barrier and formed a low, flat island exposed to the ravaging elements and particularly those of the wind and sea, which ultimately sealed its fate.

At its peak, Old Winchelsea was a prosperous fishing village with some 700 houses and about 50 inns and taverns, implying a population of around 3,000 to 5,000 people. It had a well-established infrastructure known for the landing of kings as well as pirates, along with its own mint. So when one storm and flood affected half of the town, the results were devastating: 'Beside the hovels of the salt makers and the storehouses of the fishermen, and the bridges and mills, more than 300 houses in the same village with a number of churches, by the violence of the rising water were submerged.' The chronicler Raphael Holinshed (Chronicles, 1577 edn) wrote about the accompanying windstorm, of which 'the like had not been lightie knowne, and seldome, or rather never, heard of by men alive'. But it was his description of the mountainous sea, its far encroachment and power that were most colourful: 'The sea, forced contrary to its natural course flowed twice without ebbing, yielding such roaring that the same was heard a far distance from the shore.' The chronicler noted how in neighbouring Hertburne tall ships perished. During the thirteenth century the sea continued to breach the shingle barrier, which extended across the present area of Rye Bay from Fairlight to Dungeness, and the flood of 1 October was the start of many incursions, leading to a complete demise around 1287, when the settlement subsequently moved inland. The storm was equally devastating along the Friesland coast, which sustained what was described as 'irreparable damage' as the rivers flowing into the sea were forced back by the surging sea, flooding meadows, mills, bridges and houses.

VENI, CREATOR SPIRITUS

In the spring of 1251, on 21 March, Matthew Paris (Chronicles, 1872–84 edn) reported a coastal flood 'overflowed its usual bounds in parts of England, inflicting no little damage with the shores covered to a depth of 6 feet [1.8m] more than has ever been seen', which flooded areas in Lincolnshire and Kent. The summer of 1251 was deemed a very hot one, with a good and early harvest. The heat soon spawned many thunderstorms in May, June, August and September and these were accompanied by intense rains and episodes of flash flooding in a number of places throughout England and Ireland. The violent thunderstorms started on 19 May 1251 and Paris described the formation thus: 'A thick cloud arose in the morning over the whole world, as it seemed, darkening east as well as west, south as well as north, and thunder was heard as if at a great distance, with lightning preceding it. . . . The thunder and lightning approached, one clap being more terrible than the others, as if the sky bore down on the earth, the ears and hearts of all who heard being suddenly struck dumb.' The storm had near-fatal consequences for Queen Eleanor of Provence when a single bolt of lightning struck a chimney attached to the Queen's bedroom at Windsor Castle (where she was staying with King Henry III and her sons), reducing the fireplace to rubble. In neighbouring Windsor forest thirty-five oaks were struck by lightning and many left splintered.

Although not strictly flood-related, the account by Matthew Paris (Chronicles, 1872–84 edn, vol. 5, p. 263) of the storm at St Albans is, in the words of Paris himself, certainly worthy of note:

> . . . the brethren of the Preachers, or Minors, were received for shelter and meals, and could not by the earnest appeal of the monk who received and provided for them be restrained from going out, the storm not having ceased: and on going out of the town they saw meeting them a torch like a kind of drawn sword, and thunder and a dreadful murmuring contained afterwards in the road, which was a public street and worn nearly smooth by men and carriages. And turning aside they signed themselves with the cross and began

St Albans, 19 May 1251, as a
'torch like a kind of drawn sword'
approached the brethren while they
chanted the medieval hymn 'Veni,
Creator Spiritus'. *(© Chris Chatfield)*

to invoke the Holy Ghost by singing 'Veni, Creator Spiritus,' and that which
follows it, with fear and devotion. And the thunder and lightning were dulled
and the fire passed away from them while they themselves were uninjured.

The words of the miracle-inducing hymn ran:

> *Veni, Creator Spiritus,*
> *mentes tuorum visita,*
> *imple superna gratia*
> *quae tu creasti pectora*
> (Come, Holy Spirit, Creator blest,
> and in our souls take up Thy rest;
> come with Thy grace and heavenly aid
> to fill the hearts which Thou hast made.)

Heavy rains and flash flooding followed on 29 June, particularly at Roscommon in Ireland, which killed men and cattle at Erinn. The Annals of Loch Cé (Annals, 1871 edn) noted that 'a great shower fell on the festival day of Peter and Paul so that a boat sailed all round the town at Kilmore on the Shannon, and a mill could grind in the stream which flowed from the arch to Ath-na-faithcha'. Similar reports of flooding are mentioned on 17 September, where 'the darkness was dreadful and could be felt, and there happened a great deluge of rain so that the channels of the air were uncovered to the cataracts and the clouds were seen to pour out upon the earth to destroy it'.

TURBULENT TIMES

Winchelsea experienced the violent throws of the sea once again in January 1252 during an easterly gale, at a time when the harbour was deemed a vital one to England and especially to London. The day before the flood, the storm was said to have raged day and night with a strong easterly wind (although a veering south-westerly wind occasioned much damage too), and 'with horrible roaring blasts and violent beating, drove back the waves of the sea from the shores, [and] unroofed or destroyed houses'. A great windstorm ensued, uprooting the largest oaks, stripping lead from church roofs, sinking large ships and inflicting 'great and irreparable damage', which 'however great on dry land, was manifestly ten times greater at sea'. Back at Winchelsea, the sea, 'as if indignant and furious at being driven back on the day before, covered places adjacent to the shores, and washed away and drowned many men'.

The summer of 1252 was very hot and dry. A number of chroniclers, including Matthew Paris and Robert of Gloucester, are in agreement with regard to the extremity and longevity of the heat, which started in April and lasted right through to July. The persistent high temperatures led to widespread drought, fruit crops failed, rivers dried up and fish died in large quantities. The monk and writer John de Taxater (sometimes Johannes de Taxter, de Taxster or Taxston) noted that many people died from the excessive heat that year. In Ireland, residents were even able to cross the River Shannon without getting their feet wet. During periods of such drought the soil becomes highly susceptible to increased run-off, as high-intensity rainfall cannot be quickly absorbed into the ground. Therefore, it was no surprise when the first 'great' autumn rains of 1252 arrived: 'The water floods covered the face of the earth, since the excess of the dryness of the earth could not absorb the waters, and rivers flooded so that the bridges and the mills and the houses adjoining the rivers were broken, and the woods and orchards were stripped.'

During October 1253, coastal flooding affected the north-east coasts of England. Holderness and Lincolnshire suffered inundations far inland, with many houses and their inhabitants washed away. The Thames estuary suffered a similar fate, with the loss of homes, lives and a great deal of property. The chronicler Robert Fabyan commented that the River Thames rose so high that it flooded many waterfront houses, with the loss of much valuable merchandise. In summing up 1253, Matthew Paris poignantly wrote, 'The past year was abundant in crops and fruits . . . but the gain to the earth was lost to the sea, which overflowed its banks.' This inundation had further implications in 1254 as, after the floods had receded and the months passed, farming returned to normal. However, the previously fertile land had become so saturated with salt that the crops never took and subsequently failed. Even where the sea had encroached into woodlands and orchards (some distance inland), these failed to become green, leaf, flower or bear fruit. The fruit that was produced was so dried up that it had to be destroyed. Similar conditions were experienced in Flanders, also in 1254.

The poor summer harvest of 1254 was not helped by two summer thunderstorms which produced heavy rainfall and flooding, the first in July, where it was noted that 'quite suddenly inundations of rain broke forth with violent hail of a kind not seen before, which lasted for an hour or more.' The intensity of the driving rain and sizeable hail broke the tiles on houses and stripped branches off trees. Some six weeks later, in August, another similar thunderstorm produced 'an unusual inundation of rain' particularly around St Albans. Any records of flooding were overshadowed by a lightning strike to the tower of the church of St Peter in St Albans, which 'penetrated into the upper part with a horrible crash, twisted the oaken material like a net, and what was marvellous, ground it into fine shreds'. It was said that the lightning left the whole tower smoking with an intolerable stench. But worse was to come on 20 November with the flooding of a large part of Bedford. The Burton Annals (Annals, 1864c edn) noted, 'In a sudden inundation of waters, not on the account of rain, happened this same year before the feast of St. Edmund, king and martyr, by which the greater part of Bedford was carried away, and several villages in the fens, and many people of both sexes, old and young and also infants in cradles, were submerged and lost.'

RETURN OF THE DEUCALION

Summer thunderstorms produced flash flooding in July 1256. Described by Matthew Paris (Chronicles, 1872–84 edn, vol. 5, p. 561) as an extraordinary storm of wind, driving rain, hail, thunder and vivid lightning which filled the souls of men with fear:

> The mill wheels were seen to be wrenched off their axles, and transported by the force of the waters great distances, destroying neighbouring houses. And what the waters did to the water mills, the wind did not spare to do to the windmills. The piles of bridges, stacks of hay, huts of fishermen with their nets and poles, and even babies in cradles were carried away, so that it looked as if the floods of Deucalion were come again.

Bedford, which was served by the Ouse, also suffered, with damage described as 'beyond estimation'. A block of six houses were lifted and carried away by the flash flood, the inhabitants only just able to evacuate in time, indicating the sudden nature of the event.

It is interesting to read references to Deucalion within the descriptions of events in 1256. Similar in story to that of the Noachian flood, there are many versions of the Deucalion. Based on Greek mythology, it was said that when Zeus decided to destroy the men of the Bronze Age he poured heavy rain and flooded Hellas so that all men were destroyed, except a few. It was Deucalion who was instructed to build a chest, in which he and his wife Pyrrha (daughter of Epimetheus and Pandora) floated for nine days and nights, finally landing on Mount Parnassus. According to Greek mythology, Mount Parnassus was named after Parnassos, the son of Kleodora and Kleopompous. Parnassos was leader of a city which was flooded by torrential rain. It was said that citizens ran from the flood, following the howling of wolves, up the mountain slope. Maybe this is why the Deucalion flood legend mentions Mount Parnassus, but there are many other versions of this story, some of which say that Deucalion landed on Mount Othrys in Thessaly.

The Deucalion floods were again remembered on 28 December 1256, by Matthew Paris (Chronicles, 1872–84 edn), who wrote, 'There was such a deluge of rain that the surface of the earth was covered and it looked as if the time of Deucalion were returned. Whence the furrows assumed the appearance of caves, or caverns of water, and the rivers crossed the meadows, and the whole country making it look like seas.' Paris mentioned that one river in northern England carried away seven large wooden and stone bridges, mills and neighbouring houses. Although he does not identify the river or give the location of the bridges, he does mention what appears to be a thunderstorm, which may have spawned a tornado at the time: 'On this memorable day [28 December 1256], a certain fierce whirlwind disturbed the air and darkened it like unto night, accompanied with violent hail; and the clouds became thickened, emitting lightning and darting forth coruscating and terrible flashes. The thunder obviously sounded a sad prophecy. For it was in the middle of winter and the cold was more like that of February.'

PROTOMARTYR ALBAN

The heavy rains and floods between August 1256 and February 1257, in the words of Matthew Paris (Chronicles, 1872–84 edn), were 'beyond measure': 'From the time of the Assumption of the Blessed Virgin until the Purification rain did not cease to fall in deluges daily, the roads became impassable and the fields were made sterile, whence by the end of autumn the grain putrefied in the ear.' This period of storminess is corroborated by *The Lanercost Chronicle* (Chronicles, 1839 edn), which noted, 'In this year there was throughout all England and Scotland much corruption of the air and inundation of rain.'

Writing about the weather of August 1257, John de Oxenedes (Chronicles, 1859 edn) described how a 'fast and procession', in desperate times, stopped the incessant deluge, 'When a great and numerous congregation of the faithful, and the convent, celebrating a fast in solemn procession, carried the martyr Alban to St. Mary in the meadows, as was usual in such times of peril. By this the tempest was made immediately to cease and so, I may add, the crops and fruits were saved and were in general abundant.' The martyr Alban referred to here is St Alban, a protomartyr of Britain. According to Bede's *Ecclesiastical History of the English People* (1969 edn), Alban was a pagan living at the Roman settlement of Verulamium (St Albans), who converted to Christianity and was executed by beheading on a hill above the town. St Albans Abbey, Hertfordshire, was later founded near this site. Bede tells several legends associated with the story of Alban's execution, one of which says that on his way to the execution, Alban had to cross a river and, finding the bridge full of people, he made the waters part and crossed over on dry land. The executioner was so impressed with Alban's faith that he converted to Christianity on the spot, and refused to kill him. Another executioner was quickly found and legend has it that his eyes dropped out of his head when he finally executed Alban.

The summer downpours and associated floods did not last long (although probably not through the divine intervention of the martyr Alban) and this led to a good late-August and September harvest, but what was not harvested by early autumn perished. The uncharacteristic warmth of the autumn and winter, along with persistent rainfall, led to what some perceived as a complete shift in the season, with the absence of the expected cold and frost. Matthew Paris (Chronicles, 1872–84 edn) wrote, 'The past year was sterile and meagre, whatever was sown in the winter, whatever was shewing promise by flowering in spring, whatever ripened in summer, the floods of autumn chocked it. For there was neither a temperate nor serene day, nor was the surface of the lakes hardened up by the frost, as is usual, nor were icicles hanging, but the continued inundations of rain thickened the air until the Purification of the Blessed Virgin [about 2 February].'

FLOODS AND FAMINE

Summer thunderstorms in 1258 brought unhappiness to a large part of western Britain between Shrewsbury and Bristol, including areas around Bridgnorth, Worcester, Tewkesbury, Gloucester and along the Bristol Channel. A thunderstorm appeared to have started in the west and moved towards the Midlands, slowly building as it moved inland towards Shrewsbury to the west of Birmingham. During the passage of this thunderstorm there was a high volume of localised rain along the high ground and tributaries of the River Severn, and by the time the storm reached Shrewsbury the rivers were high, starting to flow swollen and fast towards Bristol and the Bristol Channel. The Annals of Tewkesbury (Annals, 1864b edn, p. 162) recorded:

A great tempest of flooding rain, snow, ice, heavy thunder and horrible lightning happened suddenly before the feast of St. John the Baptist [24 June] covering the country beyond the banks of the River Severn from Shrewsbury to Bristol. And by this flood all grass likewise adjoining the Severn and the crops were lost and destroyed, displeasing both to men and animals. Submerged in the same were horses, and many men and children of both sexes.

Continual and persistent rain in the autumn of 1258 led to misery and famine as the corn crop became rotted and ruined, resulting in desperate times for many: 'The poor devoured horse flesh, the bark of trees and things still worse, while multitudes died of starvation.' The autumn flooding remained long in the memory of those who endured it. The Annals of both Tewkesbury (Annals, 1864b edn) and Dunstable (Annals, 1866b edn) could not help compare the ferocity of the flooding to that of previous years: 'This past year was very dissimilar to all previous, that is, it was unhealthy and mortal, stormy and exceedingly rainy, so much so, that, although in summer time the harvest and crops and an abundance of fruit seemed promising, yet in the time of autumn continual heavy rains choked the corn, fruit and also vegetables.'

THE BATTLE OF EVESHAM

The events of August 1265 changed history, but the influence of a sudden storm added to the climax of one of the most notable battle campaigns of the thirteenth century: the Battle of Evesham, Worcestershire. Following his battle victory at Lewes in 1264, Simon de Montfort, Earl of Leicester (also regarded as the father of the English Parliament), had controlled the kingdom, with King Henry III effectively his prisoner along with his son Prince Edward (who later became Edward I). The prince soon escaped custody and joined forces with Gilbert de Clare (Gilbert the Red), eighth Earl of Gloucester, who, with the nobles of the Welsh Marches, assembled what was to be a strong and victorious army to defeat de Montfort. However, this was no straightforward battle, with the weather of the day clearly influencing morale and producing very difficult conditions.

On 4 August 1265, a thunderstorm moved south-east towards Evesham from north Wales, accompanied by rain, thunder and lightning. The darkness was described as being so great that during dinner, the inhabitants of Evesham could hardly see what they were eating. Conditions during the battle were described by Bartholomew de Cotton (1859 edn), who wrote, 'The day became dark, the sun withdrew his rays, there was an earthquake at the place, thunder muttered and frequent lightning shone forth.' Britton (1937, p. 112) quoted the verse of Robert of Gloucester, who drew biblical comparisons with the weather at the time of the crucifixion of Christ:

> And there with Jesus Christ was very ill pleased
> As he showed by tokens both terrible and true,
> For as it to himself befell, when he died on the cross,
> Also while the good men at Evesham were slain,
> There arose, as in the north-west, a dark storm
> So black and so sudden that many were terrified;
> And it overcast all the land, so that we might hardly see;
> A more fearful than it might not on earth be.
> A few drops of rain exceeding large there fell.

It was perceived that such a storm was a displeasing sign from the heavens, poetically compared to the biblical storm during the crucifixion of Christ. Summer rainfall such as this at the height of the battle must have had some influence, particularly on the terrain and visibility, as well as on morale. Such high-rainfall events are often short-lived but it is clear that the coincidence of this with the climax of the campaign was deemed a fearful signal. In the end, Simon de Montfort and his army were heavily outnumbered and eventually defeated. He was killed, decapitated and mutilated, and his head was displayed around the country as a warning of what happened to people who rebelled against the king.

RAIN AND EARTHQUAKES

In April 1268, the Oseney Annals (Annals, 1869a edn) recorded 'inundations of rain and runnings of water, very terrible, and enduring for fifteen days'. This was followed in September by an account by William of Newburgh of a 'very great tempest of wind and rain, and a commotion of the air, by land and sea, through which much evil resulted in divers parts. For houses were felled, trees uprooted, seed shaken out of the ground and rotted, many cattle killed and ships sunk and broken to pieces. There was this year a wet and stormy winter and one full of diseases.'

Forty days of heavy rain, inviting comparison with biblical times, flooded areas surrounding the Thames, during February and March 1270. The Oseney Annals referred to 'so much rain and pouring out of water, that before or after the deluge of Noah, such a terrible one had not been seen, and, it was said, not of such duration, for it lasted for forty days and more.' The River Thames was said to have risen so high in London that waterside sellers drowned and all merchandise perished or was lost. Apart from the obvious human tragedy, the economic loss of such merchandise would also been very costly; by the late thirteenth century, London had become one of the trading and manufacturing capitals of Europe, producing everything from woollen cloth to weapons.

A thunderstorm of 'frightening proportions' affected Canterbury, Kent in 1271. Some writers mentioned April, others September (11th or 18th); indeed these could be two separate events, but the descriptions of the events are very similar and certainly well merit discussion because of the extreme nature of the flooding and the loss of life that ensued. Both sides of the English Channel were affected, and in Burgundy, France, 'There were such rains and earthquakes that it was thought to be like a second Deluge, and houses were carried off by its inundations, and stone bridges broken; crops and vines laid to waste and submerged.'

More graphic accounts are contained in writings of John Everisden, who noted that violent rain fell suddenly on Canterbury, that the greater part of the city was suddenly inundated, and 'there was such swelling of waters that the crypt of the church and the cloisters of the monastery were filled with water.' Walter de Hemingburgh (Chronicles, 1848–9 edn, vol. 1, p. 340) noted:

There was at Canterbury such a flood of rain, with thunder, lightning and tempest such that two very old men had never heard or seen anything like it for prolonged thunder, for it was if one horrible clap sounded for the whole of the aforesaid day and night, and such floodwater followed that trees and hedges were over thrown, whereby to proceed was not possible either to men or horses, and many were imperilled by the force of the waters flowing in the streets and in the houses of citizens. A very great famine followed throughout the whole kingdom.

Cambridge and Norwich were flooded to such an extent in 1273 that it was said to have been 'almost equalled to those of 1258 . . . while in some parts of England they appeared to have exceeded in violence'. This is an interesting comparison between events some fifteen years apart. The rains lasted 'a night and a day' and in Cambridge the flood waters rose 5ft (1.5m) above the main bridge in the city.

An 'earthquake' signalled coastal floods in September 1275 as Gervase of Canterbury (1879 edn) mentioned: 'A great earthquake happened in many kingdoms, and chiefly in England, and floods of water also about maritime towns.' Walter de Hemingburgh (Chronicles, 1848–9 edn) noted, 'In the year of the Lord 1275 on the ides of September, there was a general earthquake in London and in the kingdom of England, both in camps and towns, habitations and fields.' It is difficult to establish whether the earthquake and the marine inundations are directly related, as the word 'earthquake' was often used to describe thunder. It could have been a tremor, and therefore this should not be discounted. There have been a number of similar tremors, especially in eastern Britain, and those in 1089, 1382, 1580, 1692 and 1884 are well recorded.

The Chronicle of Bury St Edmunds reported localised flooding in Bury St Edmunds, Suffolk (where the storm was thought to be at its strongest), as well as into Essex and Cambridgeshire around 10 October 1277, which apparently lasted two days and a night. 'Such a flood followed this cloud-burst that in some places men and cows, sheep and other domestic animals in the fields were overcome at night by the storm and drowned. Houses, walls, trees and some buildings which stood in the way of the flood were completely overthrown.' In December the sea inundated Reiderland, in the Netherlands, where fifty villages were washed away with great loss of life.

Cheshire experienced a marine and fluvial flood during February 1279, with flood damage at Stanlow. The reports of flooding at this location originate largely from the Cistercian abbey that was founded at Stanlow (or Stanlaw) in 1178. Built on the low-lying marsh, Stanlow Point, the abbey had an eventful history spanning nearly 400 years. The floods in 1279 were described by Wallis (1923): 'The inundations of the sea were of an extraordinary nature. The church and the buildings were flooded to the depth of 4 or 5 feet with salt water, part of the site was washed away, and there was imminent danger of the whole becoming permanently water-logged and uninhabitable.' Later, the tower of the abbey was felled by a great gale in 1287 and further floods (and a fire) in 1289 caused much damage; by 1296 all the monks had left. The site of Stanlow Abbey was between the junction of the rivers Gowey and Mersey, but is largely inaccessible today as the site has become a major oil refinery. What was described in the Chester Annals (1887 edn) as a very unusual and excessive current resulted in 'the bridge' at Chester being destroyed and carried away. This was probably a reference to the Dee bridge. It is difficult to establish the full sequence of events but it seems that either a coastal inundation from the Irish Sea funnelled up the rivers Mersey and Dee; or perhaps a high fluvial outflow from excess rainfall could have amplified the river as described.

It was the historic city of Oxford that experienced a sudden and violent inundation of flood waters in April 1280, the like of which 'had not been seen in this time of year for thirty years or more'. Then followed an August flash flood; the exact locations affected are unclear but the sources hint towards a storm which moved between Cambridgeshire and Norfolk. It was described in the text of Bartholomew de Cotton (1859 edn), a Norwich monk and great historical writer for Norfolk: 'There was such an inundation of rain, and such violent floods of water followed, that men and women, old and young, and herds in the fields were drowned, mills and bridges, houses and trees, were submerged, and hay and corn in most places was carried away.'

GREAT INUNDATIONS

If there was one year that was notable for its succession of devastating floods, then it was probably 1287, with notable events occurring in the United

Kingdom during January, February and December of that year. The cusp of 1287 saw the first of the great inundations and these are mentioned by a number of sources, including *The Chronicle of Bury St Edmunds* and *The Chronicle of Florence of Worcester* (Chronicles, 1854 edn, p. 374):

On the night of the Circumcision [meaning the Feast of the Circumcision of Christ, 1 January] the wind was so violent, and the sea so stormy, at Yarmouth, Dunwich, Ipswich and other places in England, as well as on the coasts of other countries bordering on the sea, that many buildings were thrown down, especially in that part of England called the Fens: nearly the whole district was converted into a lake and unhappily a great number of men were overtaken by the floods and drowned.

Bartholomew de Cotton suggested that the flood started at around midnight on 31 December: 'There was a great inundation of the waters and the sea, so that, by the floods, boats to the number of 180 at Kirkhale and one sailor perished.' It is more than likely that Kirkhale (Kirkharle) is a reference to what was then known as Kirk Harle parish, Northumberland. The Oseney Annals are connected to Oseney Abbey, Oxford, and contain the history of the monastery between 1016 and 1347. These annals also mention events of 31 December and 1 January: 'On the feast of the Lord's Circumcision, a most strong wind began to blow from the eastern points (which is called Eurus) and . . . the greater part of the town of St. Botolph's was submerged and men and a numberless multitude of cattle perished. There was a similar inundation in Essex and in several other eastern parts; nor was such a dreadful sea flood seen in those parts for thirty years past or more' (Annals, 1869a edn). It is interesting to note the Greek mythological reference to Eurus, who was the god of the east wind and was known as the wind that brought warmth and rain. The Dunstable Annals (Annals, 1866b edn) also mentioned this rain and flood: 'There was a great inundation of rain and the northerly sea from the Humber to Yarmouth overflowed its usual bounds, and in some parts to a breadth of three leagues, in other to four, everything being submerged. A great magnitude of men, sheep and cattle were destroyed.' The unit of measurement, the league, although no longer officially used in western measurements, was devised in Ancient Rome and came to the Romans via the Greeks and the Persian parasang (which was an ancient Persian unit of distance corresponding to approximately 3.5 miles). In theory, a league expresses the distance a person (or a horse) could walk in one hour of time, usually about three miles. Therefore, the flooding covered a distance of some 9 to 12 miles (14–19km) at Yarmouth in that year.

On 17 December 1287 a storm surge travelled down the east coast of England with the most tragic of consequences: 'The sea, as well by the violence of the winds as by their boisterousness and raging impetuosity, began to be disturbed by a dense cloud and, with huge rushes, broke through the flat shores, disturbing its customary bounds, and occupying fields, villages and other places on its confines, and also inundating parts which no one remembered seeing before covered by the waters of the sea in a cycle of a thousand ages past.' Bartholomew de Cotton wrote, 'About midnight thunder was heard and on the Wednesday following there was a great inundation of waters of the sea.' This inundation coincided with high tide and the flood affected the low-lying coast between the Humber and Kent, and particularly large areas of East Anglia around the Norfolk Broads. John of Oxnead (Johannis de Oxenedes; Chronicles, 1859 edn) described how the night flood waters caught many by surprise and at midnight men and women rushed out of their houses in bed clothes, holding babies asleep in cradles and seeking a safe place of refuge. Some tried to climb trees, but the strength of the flood was too much to contend with, and they drowned. Large numbers of cattle and freshwater fish were destroyed through the vast inundations of sea water, and houses along with all of their contents 'were removed from their deep foundations with irreparable damage'. In the village of Hickling, Norfolk, twenty people drowned as the flood waters rose a reported 1ft above the high altar of the Priory Church (often referred to as the Priory of Canons). All the canons except two fled; the two remaining were said to have sheltered horses in their dormitories for safety. Bartholomew de Cotton noted that, as well as Hickling, the coastal villages of Horsey and Waxham and inland Martham (as well as a few other, smaller neighbouring villages) suffered casualties, with around 200 people reported drowned. These locations circle Hickling Broad, and examination of these on a map shows that it is possible that the flood affected a much wider area around this low-lying stretch of county.

Flood water on the night of 17 December 1287 caught many by surprise. (© *Chris Chatfield*)

Further south-west along the Broads, the Abbey of St Benedict of Hulme in Horning was infiltrated by a river torrent which surrounded the building. John de Oxenedes (Chronicles, 1859 edn) quoted what could have been poignantly said: '*Abissus vallavit me, et pelagus operuit caput meum*', meaning 'the Abbey has walled me in, the ocean has covered my head'. This can be interpreted as a distinct reference to the prophecy of Jonah: 'And thou hast cast me forth into the deep in the heart of the sea, and a flood hath compassed me: all thy billows, and thy waves have passed over me.'

The abbey has an interesting history and in 1020 the manor of Horning was given by King Canute (or Knut) to the Abbey of St Benedict of Hulme. It was the same King Canute who wisely said, after failing to command the sea to go back, 'Let all men know how empty and worthless is the power of kings. For there is none worthy of the name but God, whom heaven, earth and sea obey.' Interestingly, the village sign today at Horning reads, 'The name [Horning] means, "The folk who live on the high ground between

71

rivers".' Further south-east of Horning on the coast at Great Yarmouth, around 100 people drowned and the stone wall of the main cemetery was destroyed by the sea for a length of 60ft (18m). In total, it was thought that some 500 lost their lives along the east coast. The gale-driven North Sea storm surge made its way down the coast and towards the Straits of Dover. During the thirteenth century Old Winchelsea was attacked several times by French marauders and a number of powerful coastal storms; it stood strong, but it was the incursions of the sea which proved its greatest enemy and by the end of 1287 the fate of the town was sealed as the storm surge made its way into the English Channel and removed all signs of what was left of town and beach. It was said that this one storm created 'a tempest of all tempests' at Winchelsea, with waves of an unprecedented height totally removing all in their wake, including sea walls that offered little or no protection to what was left. Old Winchelsea was soon gone forever and a new town of the same name was later constructed some two miles away on higher ground. In Europe, particularly Friesland (northern coastal parts of the Netherlands), Flanders (Belgium and southern coastal Netherlands) and Denmark, the dykes that held back the North Sea failed. Hundreds of acres of low-lying land were affected and tragically it was estimated that 50,000 to 80,000 people lost their lives. A new bay, called Zuiderzee (Southern Sea), was created over former farmland and this started yet more years of building dykes and creating polders to push back the flood waters of the Zuiderzee.

TORRENTS OF WATER

The weather of the year 1288 was known for two things: the long hot summer that lasted at peak for some five weeks and led to abundant harvests (and also a drought that claimed many lives), and, more devastating, the massive sea floods of 4 February 1288. A number of writers and chronicles, including Everisden, Gervase of Canterbury and the Oseney Annals, mentioned the storms of the 3rd and floods of 4 February, and the consensus is that these occurred in February 1288 as stated. It should be noted that the Worcester and Dunstable Annals record this in 1287, but it is possible that these are being confused with the floods of the previous December. The storm system started on the night of 3 February and *The Chronicle of Florence of Worcester* (Chronicles, 1854 edn, p. 376) recorded:

> On the third of the none of February, about nightfall, flashes of light were suddenly and unexpectedly seen at St. Edmunds [Bury St Edmunds], there having been no signs prognosticating it: and at the same instant, there was a tremendous crash, I will not say of thunder, followed by an insufferable stench. The storm was accompanied by visible sparks of fire, which fearfully dazzled the eyes of the beholders. The tower of the church of Barnwell was set on fire by the violence of the thunderstorm and further damage was done to the convent there, and one third part of the town was prey to the flames.

On the 4th, the sea rose 'to such an extent in Thanet and round about, and in the marshes of Romney and all the adjacent parts, that all the dykes were demolished and nearly all the ground was covered from the great dyke at Appledore to Winchelsea both towards the east and the west'. The Thames estuary suffered also, and the inundation from the seas was described as so violently powerful that 'for one day and night, contrary to its ordinary usage and the course of nature, it was seen to flow and reflow four times alternatively'. This resulted in some substantial flooding in London along the banks of the Thames in areas which, up until this time, usually withstood the force of the sea. Hundreds of properties were flooded and the Oseney Annals described this occurring 'over a much greater distance than any mortal at any time had seen'. Further down the Thames, villages and fields were 'swallowed up and countless men and innumerable cattle . . . were drowned'. Along the east coast, at Spalding, a monastery was damaged by the 'impetuous deep waters which flowed and covered them'. The building of the friars preachers at Yarmouth (which at the time was next to the sea) was submerged unexpectedly by the flood waters. The neighbouring town of Yarmouth also experienced high levels of coastal flooding, in which it was said that buildings were 'submerged and blotted out'. The North Sea coast between Spalding and the Thames estuary appeared to have suffered the most during the storm surge in 1288, but it also continued down the North Sea and towards the Netherlands, where similar levels of inundation were experienced.

Thunderstorm-induced flood waters on 19 July 1289 (and similarly during the summer of 1290) caused such crop destruction that the price of wheat increased sevenfold – from three pence to two shillings. William of Rishanger described how a sudden inundation of rain, thunder and lightning drowned the crops, especially those of the valued wheat, 'so for nearly 40 years, until the death of King Edward there existed a dearness of crops and especially wheat'. According to *The Chronicle of St Werburgh*, vast areas of cultivated land alongside the Mersey were abandoned to floods in 1294. This was most likely the result of the very wet August, September and October, when persistent rain meant that little or no corn could be harvested. In October, the River Thames flooded a number of areas around Rotherhithe, Bermondsey, Tothill and Westminster. The Bermondsey Annals (Annals, 1866 edn) recorded that 'torrents of the waters of the Thames overpassed their usual limits . . . and there happened a great breach at Rotherhithe and the plains at Bermondsey. . . . similarly it reached the cottages of the merchants at the fair of Westminster and forced them to strengthen the dwellings with taller stakes.' These Thames-side tradesmen were great sufferers, and as the fourteenth century approached, so did the severe, cold, hard winters and dangerous frozen waters of the River Thames.

Chapter 5

THE FOURTEENTH CENTURY

For the inundation of rain consumed nearly all the seed, so that now was seen the fulfilment of the prophecy of Isaiah.

(Vita et mors Edwardi secundi, *de la Moor, 1883*)

F lood reports at the beginning of the fourteenth century appear sporadic, and the weather after 1300 was largely influenced by a succession of severe cold winters, especially during 1302/3, 1305/6 and 1309/10. The year 1309 saw a great frost and masses of encrusted ice on the River Thames. The ice was so thick that people danced in the middle of the river and hunted hares with dogs. As the thaw started, the swollen waters laden with large chunks of ice damaged a number of bridges, including London Bridge. When the thaw came to Salisbury, the cathedral was suddenly inundated. King Edward II, who was there at the time, was forced to leave for fear of being drowned.

Thomas Walsingham's *Historia Anglicana* (1862 edn) described 1313 as an uneventful year for weather, 'neither cloudy nor serene, neither disturbed or calm'. But the rain and cold soon arrived, and 1314, 1315 and 1316 were notable for their deluges and associated famine. Matthew of Westminster wrote of 1314, 'Now in the kingdom there were such outpourings of rain and inundations of water with the unusual disturbance of the air, that crops and victuals were consumed and in one year not seven serene days together could be found.' Ravensdale (1974) noted, 'Even Cottenham (the Fens, River Ouse) with its arable above the twenty-four foot contour did not escape the flooding. In 1314, four tenants were in mercy, on account of a watercourse in the fields.'

The following year fared no better, especially during the wet summer of July and August. Britton (1937) quoted from the Latin title *Vita et mors Edwardi secundi* (Life and Death of Edward II; de la Moor, 1883 edn, p. 214):

Now this past year there was such an abundance of rain that men hardly gathered any crops for sale or stored it safely in the barn. For the inundation of rain consumed nearly all the seed, so that now was seen the fulfilment of the prophecy of Isaiah, and in several places hay was so hidden under water that it could neither be cut nor gathered. Sheep also perished in flocks and the animals died of a sudden murrain.

Preston (1929) wrote, 'In crossing the Thames in a state of flood in July 1315, the Abbot Richard Clive and several of his principal officials were drowned.' Anderson (1970) sourced this as happening a year later: 'In 1316 the then Abbot of Abingdon and a number of his monks tried to cross by ferry (at Abingdon) when the river was in flood. Their boat upset and all were drowned.' There does indeed seem to be confusion in a number of sources between the years 1314 and 1316, basically because the conditions in these years were very similar. Britton (1937) also noted some date confusion and 'consequent overlapping in the very many accounts which have survived various historians as to the period of famine and bad harvests which occurred in the years 1314 to 1316 or 1317. There was at least one very wet year, and probably two, in the period.' Indeed, during 1316 the heavy summer and autumn rains produced much misery through floods and famine, and people were reduced to eating horses and dogs.

RAGING WATERS

It is interesting that Britton (1937, p. 134) has quoted an account by Robert of Reading that vividly described a severe storm in late June 1323. This account was more likely a tornado which disturbed the waters around Cowick, East Yorkshire, just south of Selby:

. . . for about the feast of St John Baptist there was a furious tempest and dark whirlwind at the manor of Cowick, not far from the cell of Selby. . . .

at the ninth hour, the king with his courtiers being at meat at the table, suddenly a dark cloud obscured them, so that, in the courtyard, the servants by reason of the great darkness, could hardly see those resting there. Then the wind rushed into that thick darkness with such violence that oaks of wonderful size and other trees were torn up by the roots, one, indeed, being twisted in two at the middle, and another cloven from the top downwards. . . . Thirdly, with a horrible turmoil, the waters flowing around were thrown violently from their channels.

The events of 1326 along the Thames were most unusual: an inundation of the river between Stratford and Tilbury during a period of severe drought produced an interesting flood. The *Croniques de London* (Chronicles, 1844 edn) noted that in this year, 'there was a great dryness of rivers and fountains, so that there was a great shortage of water in several countries. . . . In this time, for the lack of sweet water, the sea flowed up so far that the water of the Thames was salt.' It was even suggested that the River Thames was saline for a whole year.

November 1334 brought marine floods. *The Chronicle of Adam Murimuth* (Chronicles, 1889 edn) described 'a great inundation of the sea throughout all the kingdom of England and mostly affecting the Thames'. Sea walls were broken down and many animals drowned. What was once fruitful land became converted into salt marshes and their fertility could not be restored for many years.

Another restless year was experienced in 1338, especially by those in Kilkenny, Ireland. The Annals of Ireland were written by the Franciscan friar John Clyn of the Convent of Friars Minors, Kilkenny, and Thady Dowling, Chancellor of Leighlin. Kilkenny is situated on the River Nore and the city has a long history of flooding, largely associated with the River Nore and its tributary the River Breagagh, which converge at Kilkenny. The flooding that occurred on 17 November 1338 was described in detail by John Clyn (Britton, 1937, p. 138–9): 'There was a great inundation of water, the like of which had not been seen for 40 years previously, in which bridges, mills and buildings were overthrown and carried away; the waters did not reach or cover the foot of the great altar, or the steps of the altar, of the whole Abbey of the Friars Minor at Kilkeney.' The high altar was said to be one of the largest and most beautiful of its kind in Ireland at the time. Its table was made from the now famous Kilkenny black marble.

Back across the Irish Sea, the year 1339 was one that went down in the history books of Newcastle upon Tyne. During some 400 years of occupation, it is known that the Romans built bridges across the Tyne, including one built by the Emperor Hadrian around AD 120, on a similar site to where the present Newcastle Swing Bridge stands. Completed in 1320, the medieval stone bridge across the River Tyne was constructed on the same site as the Roman Bridge. The bridge was about 711ft (217m) long and about 15ft (4.5m) wide between parapets. Just nineteen years after the bridge was completed, a heavy flood occurred on Tyneside. The bridge was damaged and had to be repaired.

The Chronicle of Lanercost Abbey (Chronicles, 1839 edn) provided an account of events on 12 August: 'In the same year on the third day before the assumption of the glorious Virgin, in the night, at Newcastle upon Tyne, there happened a marvellous inundation of waters whereby the wall of the town near to Walkenowe was broken down for a length of 6 perches, and 160 men and 7 priests, and more were drowned.' A perch is an old unit of measurement, with one perch equivalent to 16.5ft (approximately 5m); therefore the structural damage to the wall is estimated at some 100ft (30m). Other sources mention this event and some suggested that the fatality figure was more likely around 140 persons, but even so, this was a true tragedy, and one that was to be repeated, but in much worse measure, more than 400 years later, in 1771.

CISTERCIAN CONVENT

Across the border and into Scotland, the biblical descriptions of flooding in East Lothian on 7 September 1358 in the *Chronica Gentis Scotorum* (Chronicles, 1871 edn, p. 377) made interesting reading: 'On the vigil of the nativity of the Blessed Virgin, such a great inundation of rain burst forth in parts of Lothian that from the time of Noah until the present day the like had not been known in the realm of Scotland, whereby the waters swelled up and overflowed their channels and banks, and spread over fields, villages, towns and monasteries.'

A courageous nun warns the flood waters with an image of the Virgin Mary at Haddington in 1358. (© *Chris Chatfield*)

One location to suffer was a convent of Cistercian nuns in the village of Abbey. At the time, Abbey was an established hamlet of the parish of Haddington and a market town in East Lothian. *The National Gazetteer* (Hamilton, 1868) described the locality as having an undulating surface, and how 'the River Tyne flows through a very delightful district, and the whole of the parish is in a high state of cultivation. The Garleton Hills, clothed with beautiful plantations, rises in the North.' The topography of the Garleston Hills could easily have influenced the passage of any heavy rains, leading to localised flash flooding. At its peak the hill rises to 610ft (186m) above sea level, with a slightly lower outcrop to the south-east.

The Cistercian convent at Abbey was founded in 1178 by Ada, Countess of Northumberland and mother of Malcolm IV. The *Ordnance Gazetteer of Scotland* (1884–5) included a colourful account of the flood water at this location: 'The river, though adding much to the beauty and comfort of

Haddington, has at various dates occasioned great damage in times of flood. In 1358 the convent was on the point of being swept away by one of those inundations; but, according to legend, was preserved by the courageous conduct of one of the nuns, who seized an image of the Virgin Mary and threatened to throw it into the flood, unless the impending destruction was averted.' The damage was described in the *Chronica Gentis Scotorum* (Chronicles, 1871 edn, p. 377):

> . . . it overturned from their foundations, and destroyed in its rush, stone walls in villages and houses and very strong bridges. Also great oaks and stout trees standing near the rivers were torn up at the roots whence they were violently carried down to the edge of the sea. Crops also and cut stubble, exposed in places to be dried, were, with damage, dragged away from the use of men and places far and near.

STORM OF THE CENTURY

Then came what some regard as the storm of the fourteenth century. In fact, 15 January 1362 produced what is considered one of the most severe storms recorded in the literature prior to events in 1703. Some twentieth-century writers have attempted to compare this event, which largely affected southern and eastern England, with the storms of October 1987. But the reported fatalities (estimated into the hundreds of thousands) as a result of a North Sea flood along the Danish, Dutch and German coasts render such a comparison unwarranted. The Chronicle of John of Reading (Johannis de Reading; 1914 edn, p. 150) described the events:

> In the year of grace 1362, the 10th of our lord Pope Innocent, and 36th of the reign of Edward III, king of England, the king in the winter was at Windsor; on the 15th day of January, the west or south wind called Affricus threw down and broke into pieces belfries, towers, trees, buildings and other strong things, the weak things being spared, and on land, as well as by sea, irretrievably destroyed good things: there hardly remained entire a house or a tree in its course. The strength of the wind did not abate for seven days and nights following.

Among the towers referred to were Salisbury Cathedral, the original spire of which was damaged during the storm; the bell towers at Bury St Edmunds and Norwich, and the belfry of the Austin Friars in London. The cause and suffering as a result of this storm retained a theological perspective in the *Eulogium* (Chronicles, 1858–68 edn), 'whence it was believed by some that the misfortune was a scourging of God'. *The Chronicle of John Hardyng* (Chronicles, 1812 edn, p. 330) described the storm in Middle English verse:

> In the same yere was on sainct Maurys day,
> The greate winde and earth quake meruelous,
> That greately gan the people all affraye,
> So dredfull was it then and perelous,
> Specially the wind was so boistous,
> The stone walles, steples, houses and trees,
> Were blow doune in diuerse ferre countrees

On the continent, January 1362 was to be known as *Die Große Manndränke*, the large drowning of men, with extensive coastal floods claiming the lives of an estimated 100,000 people between Schleswig and the Danish coast. The powerful and rich city of Rungholt, located in Nordfriesland, northern Germany, was wiped out and over seventy villages destroyed. The coastline was changed forever.

Heavy rain, cold winters and much snow and ice prevailed between 1362 and 1377. The thawing of snow in late December 1377 (around Christmas) created a flash flood which carried blocks of ice and debris through a passage of destruction in Northumberland. The *Chronicon Angliae* (Chronicles, 1874 edn, p. 109) presented a detailed account of the snow-melt and subsequent floods:

. . . so much water prevailed in parts of Northumberland by the melting of the snows which covered the earth to a great depth, that the floods, which with very large fragments of ice, descended from the ridges of the mountains, overturned the houses of the farmers; goods which had been stacked on the ground, such as coal, millstones, wood, or crops, were carried away by the rush of waters. And, further, falling into the sea, by the strength and concussion of the said blocks of ice, certain ships were either rendered useless by the violence of the collision with the ice, or entirely submerged.

Christmas floods were recorded in December 1382, as King Richard II, who was aged 15 at the time, was prevented from spending his planned Christmas Day at Windsor as a result of the rising flood waters. Instead, he had to spend it in London at Westminster. On the eastern side of Malvern, Worcestershire, there were two houses of Benedictine monks, the priories of Great and Little Malvern. John of Malvern was a monk at Worcester and is quoted by Britton (1937, p. 148) on a number of occasions, particularly with regard to the floods of December 1382:

> . . . for two days and three nights before the feast of St. Thomas the apostle [celebrated on 21 December], there were continuous inundations of rain, whereby in various parts of England the waters increased and overflowed so much that there followed immense damage to the crops and other things . . . all the flocks and various herds of sheep were cut off, and the waters raised themselves to such a degree that men, in consideration of their lives, sought the highest floors of their houses, and the topmost parts of trees.

John of Malvern also wrote about the severe floods in Exeter, Devon, during January 1386. The flood waters were so strong that they carried away bridges and submerged many houses in the city. Exeter's battle with the River Exe was centuries long but the city remained defiant and prosperous. However, not all locations were so fortunate. In 1393 *The Melsa Chronicle* (Chronicles, 1863–8 edn) mentioned inundations of the River Humber submerging land at Tharlesthorpe, but with recurring storms exacerbating coastal erosion in this region it was not long into the fifteenth century before the settlement was completely lost to the sea.

Chapter 6

THE FIFTEENTH CENTURY

. . . there was such an abundance of rain, lightning and thunder, with freezing wind and obscurity of the air that men were struck with the fear that the crops would be chocked by the inundation of waters.

(The St Albans Chronicle)

Tharlesthorpe (Tharlsthorp), which now lies under the sea off the Holderness coast (near Spurn Head) in the East Riding of Yorkshire, was a thriving town up until the middle of the thirteenth century, but its location, vulnerable to the North Sea storm climate and the River Humber, soon brought about its demise. Once a fertile farming centre famous for its corn and livestock, the village was reported to have had well over 1,000 animals by the end the thirteenth century. Inundations from the Humber became frequent, such that by the middle of the thirteenth century the waters could no longer be held back, and the village suffered a similar fate to that of others like Frismersk and Penisthorpe. River Humber floods are mentioned in *The Melsa Chronicle* (Chronicles, 1863–8 edn) in 1400 referring to Tharlesthorpe once more, but by this time the village had long been consigned to the history books.

The Festival of the Nativity of the Blessed Virgin Mary was celebrated on 9 September, and on this date in 1400 the 'Old Bridge' at Durham was damaged – some sources suggest swept away – by a raging flood. The 'Old Bridge' is a reference to the Framwellgate Bridge over the River Wear, the earliest of Durham's bridges, built by Ranulf Flambard, one of the most powerful bishops of Durham. It was later rebuilt by Bishop Thomas Langley, consisting originally of three stone segmental ribbed arches, of seven ribs each.

WELSH CAMPAIGNS

The advent of flash flooding was to prove almost perilous to King Henry IV during his Welsh campaigns against Owen Glendower (Owain Glyndŵr), the self-proclaimed Prince of Wales, between 1402 and 1408. The Annals of Henry IV (Annals, 1866c edn) noted, 'during the vigil of the nativity of St. Mary, when the King had pitched his tent in a very pleasant meadow, where, apart from the nature of the place, nothing was to be dreaded but much rest was hoped for, suddenly in the first watch of that same night there fell such an abundance of rain as seemed to almost drown the English.' A number of writers noted King Henry's persistent bad luck when it came to the weather. Britton (1937, p. 153) published an English verse attributed to *The Chronicle of John Hardyng* (Chronicles, 1812 edn) that highlighted Henry's toilsome time in Wales:

> The kyng Henry thryce to Wales went,
> In the haye time and haruest dyuers yere,
> In euery tyme were mystes and tempestes sent,
> Of wethers foule that he had neuer power
> Glendour to noye, but euer his caryage clere
> Owen had a certayne straites and passage
> And to our hoste dyd full greate damage.
> The Kyng had neuer but tempest foule & raine,
> As longe as he was ay in Wales grounde,
> Rockes & mystes, windes & stormes euer certaine,
> All men trowed yt witches it made that stounde . . .

The prose clarifies the August to September rains and the three attempts King Henry IV made to penetrate Wales's varying climatic conditions in his efforts against Glendower.

ST ELIZABETH'S FLOOD

A North Sea storm surge affected the east coast of England and parts of northern Europe in November 1404. Some writers, for example Holinshed, placed this on the 11th; others, particularly in the Netherlands, suggested the

19th. This could be the result of a calendar discrepancy, simple transcription error or unreliability of recording; however, what happened during the month of November 1404 was another example of how vulnerable low-lying coastal areas were to storms in the North Sea. In the Annals of Henry IV (Annals, 1866c edn) it was written, 'At this time there happened in Kent and in many places unprecedented irruptions of waters, through which many mansions were washed away and animals of various kinds were drowned. And while, we are silent as to others, the lord of Canterbury and the Prior of the same place incurred the loss of a thousand pounds. At Calais also the water of the sea flowed into the town beyond the walls.'

The storm surge affected a much broader region especially along what was Flanders and Zeeland, the same area which had been flooded some twenty years earlier on 8 October 1375 when the Westfriese sea wall broke, flooding the Dutch coast. To this day the Dutch regard this event as the 'first St Elizabeth's flood'. Researchers at the Deltawerken Foundation (2004) described the damage as catastrophic: 'Around the Zuudzee, polders were diked, and within these polders, new parishes arose. Unfortunately, in 1404, everything was destroyed again. This time, a complete spit that was home to a number of small towns such as Ijzendijke and Hugevliet, which were spared in 1375, was engulfed during the flood.'

A storm crossing the North Sea led to a fateful storm surge along the Dutch coast on 19 November 1421, enhanced by heavy rains and increased fluvial output. Known as 'the second St Elizabeth floods', these brought 'death and destruction' along the Zuiderzee. Gaps in the coastline of the Grote Waard (or Groote Waard, the southern side of the present-day province of South Holland) from previous floods accentuated the severity, ultimately destroying the Grote Waard. At the lowest point inland, the flood waters reached the city of Dordrecht, where the water still remains today, as the Biesbosch was born. The western section of Zeeland-Flanders was largely spared this time, but North Beveland was ravaged. The island was hit so severely that Jan van Beieren (the governor) decided to cut taxes, so that people were able to afford vital repairs. South Beveland was also heavily affected and the parishes of Beoosten and Yerseke were put at risk. The Deltawerken Foundation (2004) suggested that thirty villages were lost, with some 2,000 lives. Other estimates suggested some seventy-two villages, with a death toll around 10,000. In the years that followed, the parishes of Schouwen and Duiveland were unable to pay their contributions to the bishop of Utrecht, because they, too, had to carry out costly repairs as a result of the floods.

STOURBRIDGE FAIR

In 1427 the great inundations which ruined fenlands not only in Lincolnshire but elsewhere in England were brought to the attention of Parliament. There were a number of notable storms this year, mostly thunderstorms, and the associated heavy rain produced flash flooding. The first instance was on 28 May after persistent rain lasted some twenty-four hours. As *The St Albans Chronicle* (Chronicles, 1870 edn) reported, 'In the fifth year of King Henry the Sixth, on the vigil of the Ascension, from the ninth hour to the ninth hour of the following day, there was such an abundance of rain, lightning and thunder, with freezing wind and obscurity of the air that men were struck with the fear that the crops would be chocked by the inundation of waters.'

A few weeks later, on 11 July, further heavy rainfall flooded hay and crops at Stourbridge Fair, Cambridge. Stourbridge Fair has a long and interesting history and it is no surprise it was included in the text of many writers, as the fair became one of the largest medieval fairs in Europe. Daniel Defoe noted in his *Tour Through the Whole Island of Great Britain*, published in 1724, 'I now draw near to Cambridge, to which I fancy I look as if I was afraid to come, having made so many circumlocutions beforehand; but I must yet make another digression before I enter the town (for in my way, and as I came in from Newmarket, about the beginning of September), I cannot omit, that I came necessarily through Stourbridge Fair, which was then in its height' (1779 edn). The fair declined not long afterwards, towards the end of the eighteenth century, and was formally abolished in 1934.

NORTH SEA

A devastating North Sea storm surge between 31 October and 1 November 1436 at Schleswig-Holstein, north-west Germany, separated Nordstrand from Pellworm. At Sylt, the town of Eidum was severely flooded, with large areas of surrounding land completely lost to the sea. The survivors of the town were forced to relocate permanently and moved to Wäästerlön (Westerland) in Söl'ring some distance north-east of the original town. During the flood, they tried to salvage what they possibly could, including the altar from the village church, which can still be seen at Westerland's Alte Dorfkirche (Old Village Church).

Another generally a wet year was experienced in 1439, particularly in Lincolnshire, *The Chronicles of the Abbey of Croyland* (Chronicles, 1908 edn) recorded: 'There was such an excess quantity of fresh water in the weirs and streams in consequence of the extraordinary rains, that the embankments around the Precinct of Croyland were unable to hold out against the force of the tempestuous torrent . . . and, being driven onward by the force of the North wind, inundated the entire surface of the adjacent common of Whaplode.' Croyland Abbey, Crowland, Lincolnshire, a Benedictine abbey dating from around 716, was the origin of *The Chronicles of Croyland*. The reference in these chronicles to Whaplode (near Holbeach and the Wash) and Croyland (Crowland) implies the influence of the River Welland in times of flood, but also the usefulness of the floodplains and commons, which absorbed such waters in the Fens.

Some of the most severe North Sea storms occurred during the fifteenth and sixteenth centuries after the onset of the Little Ice Age. These storms certainly resulted in high death tolls, as low-lying inhabited areas afforded little protection from the sea in comparison to modern-day coastal management initiatives. Areas particularly badly affected were the coastal fringes of the Netherlands, Germany and Denmark, as well as the east and south-east coasts of England.

Events on 10 April 1446 had catastrophic consequences for regions around Dordrecht in the Netherlands, where an estimated 100,000 lives were lost as a result of the violent windstorm and flood. Dordrecht has an interesting history dating back to the eleventh century (*c.* 1008). It was fortified in 1271 and soon became a thriving settlement where the Lower Merwede divided to form the Noord and Oude Maas (Old Meuse) rivers. It was these rivers and the combined North Sea floods in 1421 that inundated large areas in and around Dordrecht and resulted in the city's becoming effectively an island, 'Eiland van Dordrecht' (Island of Dordrecht). Still well populated and protected by its city walls, Dordrecht and the surrounding regions received further flood casualties in 1446. But its strategic position made it an important market city, where wine, wood and cereals were traded and so it continued to thrive. In 1572, representatives of twelve Dutch cities gathered in Dordrecht to declare their independence from Spain and acknowledged William of Orange as the leader of the Dutch state. But by the eighteenth century, the importance of Dordrecht started to diminish, and Rotterdam became the main city in the region. Dordrecht never surrendered to the floods and today it is still a busy port, although it later diversified its interests and founded a centre for aquatic sports. The Dutch association with water can only be described as infamous and innovative.

The River Thames flooded in March 1448, affecting Poplar and Stepney in London, and Raynham in Essex. *The Chronicle of the Grey Friars of London* (Chronicles, 1852 edn, p. 19) described this well, in typical Middle English text: 'And this yere the watter of Temse by excesse of floode the monday in Ester weke came and incresid on the londe unto Populer, and drownyd many housys and feldes and medowes, and moche of the parich of Stepney and at Raynham and other places in Essex.' (And this year the water of Thames by excess of flood the Monday in Easter week came and increased land unto Poplar, and drowned many houses and fields and meadows, and much of the parish of Stepney and at Raynham and other places in Essex.)

The summer of 1460 was supposedly one of the wettest for 100 years in Britain, and November 1470 produced a North Sea flood with fatalities estimated around 10,000, but the exact details of the event are imprecise. Lamb (1977) catalogued a notable period of storminess which resulted in two parishes being destroyed at Schleswig-Holstein in October 1476; further storms affected Friesland in December, and in November 1477, seventeen parishes were destroyed and Old Ostende was lost to the sea.

THE DUKE OF BUCKINGHAM'S WATER

Continual 'monsoon-like' rains characterised the year 1483. The River Wye in Herefordshire and the Severn in Worcestershire flooded, with 'several people drowning whilst they slept'. It was said that the waters did not abate for ten days and the occurrence became commonly known as 'The Great Water'. *Adams's Chronicle of Bristol (1623–48)* (Chronicles, 1910 edn) described a 'great flood accompanied by a severe wind' on 15 October 1483, which destroyed houses, corn and cattle and 'drowned over 200 people. Great hurt was done in Bristol where the Merchants houses and cellars were flooded. In the "Kingrode" damage was done to many ships and two were even driven onto land on "Hollow Backes".'

This report coincided with an extraordinary flood of the Severn and Wye that prevented the Duke of Buckingham (a former ally of Richard III who had now rebelled against him) from crossing to attack the King. 'In a premature attempt to seize the crown of England, Henry the Seventh's standard was hoisted by the Duke of Buckingham at Brecon in October 1483. Owing to the elements, after a ten days' struggle the attempt failed. Through heavy rain that autumn both the Wye and the Severn were so deep in flood . . . that Buckingham was cut off from his allies in the Midlands.' As a result, the Duke's army dispersed and he was captured, convicted of treason and later beheaded in Salisbury. The floods of October 1483 were to be forever known as 'The Duke of Buckingham's Water'.

Chapter 7

THE SIXTEENTH CENTURY

Du ciel viendra un grand Roy d'effrayeur (From the sky will come a great King of Terror)

(Nostradamus, Quatrain 10, 72)

D uring early 1501 there was extensive flooding in and around Oxford, but it must be said that the most noteworthy occurrence during the first quarter of the sixteenth century has to be the 'End of the World Flood' of February 1524. The potentially catastrophic and cataclysmic flood was prophesied in 1499 by the German mathematician, astronomer, astrologer and priest Johannes Stöffler, who was a professor at the University of Tübingen. During the sixteenth century, almanacs and astrology became very popular and Johannes Stöffler's *Almanach noua plurimis annis venturis inseruientia* (1499) explained the basic principles of astrology, including planetary conjunctions and their meanings. It was published in collaboration with the astronomer Jakob Pflaum of Ulm and the Almanach had a large circulation up to 1531.

In 1499, Johannes Stöffler predicted that 'a giant flood' was to occur on 20 February, with twenty different conjunctions of planets, all of which would occupy a water sign (planetary alignment in Pisces). Stöffler's forecast only anticipated a spectacular commotion of a general description; other astrologers built on this prophecy and suggested that 'The End' would incorporate a flood in London on 1st, and into 2nd, February. Both England and Europe were therefore on high flood alert between 1 and 20 February 1524.

Engraving of Johannes Stöffler, mathematician and astrologer, who predicted that there would be a second biblical flood on 20 February 1524. (© *Science Museum*)

Belief in these dates was very strong throughout Europe. The astrologer Nicolaus Peranzonus de Monte Sancte Marie suggested that a conjunction of major planets would also occur in 1524, and this strengthened the general belief in a universal deluge. The prophecy became so widely feared that thousands evacuated their homes and many built arks and defences and stockpiled food. George Tannstetter, another astrologer and mathematician, based at the University of Vienna, was one of very few at that time who denied that 'The End' would occur as predicted. His own horoscope revealed that he would live beyond 1524, and he therefore refused to believe that the calculations were correct. His counter-prophecy was largely overlooked. Randi (2005) detailed how, in many European cities, widespread fear of the impending deluge encouraged many people to build themselves boats. In Germany, Count von Iggleheim took it one step further and built a three-storey ark.

As the key dates approached, people all over Europe took refuge in boats and on high ground. It was believed that some 20,000 people fled their homes in London; many gathered on the high ground of Hampstead Heath to escape death from the flood that was to sweep London off the map. At the time, Londoners would have associated any catastrophic inundation with the flood history of the River Thames. It was thought that reaching high ground to watch this impending biblical deluge would be enough to save their lives.

The day of reckoning came – and went. It did not even rain in London on the expected date. On the continent, as terrified folk boarded ships, barges and purpose-built arks, a slight rain began to fall and everyone looked to the heavens for forgiveness. Then, the drizzle ended. In Germany, where von Iggleheim was aboard his eminent ark, the crowd, not satisfied that the deluge had occurred, rioted. Hundreds were killed in the riots and stampedes, including von Iggleheim – the crowds stoned the count to death.

Ironically, there was then some confusion in justifying the date of the actual planetary conjunction, as the planets involved were supposed to produce their combined effect on 23 February, and not the 20th. Then the astrologers recalculated and discovered they had been a mere 100 years off. As the 'end of the world flood' neither started nor caused such an end on either date – or, for that matter, since – time has shown their arguments and deliberations to have been quite irrelevant.

THE ST FELIX SURGE

Heavy rains and flash floods during the autumn of 1526 were reported in Herefordshire and Worcestershire, and 1527 and 1528 were known for two things: floods and famine. It all started in the spring of 1527 with what were described as 'incessant deluges', which prevented the corn crop from being sown. A number of chronicles suggested that it rained almost continually in June, July and September, 'after which followed a scarcity so that many died for want of bread'. Brooks and Glasspoole (1928) noted that there was further heavy rain in November and December, and by the middle of January 1528 there were great river floods. Floods were also mentioned in May, after which 'it rained every day or night till June 3rd and in May it rained 30 hours continually, which caused great floods'.

A North Sea storm surge on 5 November 1530 produced such a violent and enormous surge of water on 'Sint Felix Quade Saterdach' (St Felix's Day), that the islands of Noord-Beveland and Sint Philipsland, Zeeland, disappeared; only the tower of Kortgene was left visible. This event was to be known in the Netherlands as the 'Saint Felix Day flood'. The area east of Yerseke (known as Oost-Watering), was completely swept away. Eighteen villages and the city of Reimerswaal were badly flooded, leading to the ultimate demise of the city. Because it was situated on higher ground, it was left isolated as a small island. The land around it could not be protected despite numerous attempts to dam the area, and soon it became known as 'the drowned land of Zuid-Beveland'. The innovative and resourceful Dutch bounced back and the loss to the sea was eventually to become their gain, with the former area of Oost-Watering providing ideal subsoil for shellfish and mussel production.

THE DEVIL RIDES BY

In England, isolated reports of thunderstorms, fist-sized hail and flash flooding between 20 and 25 June 1545 were overshadowed by a tornado in Derbyshire. Lysons and Lysons (1817, p. 159–62) described it as the visiting of 'Old Nick', the Devil, who 'went to Wyndley Lane [in Duffield parish] and from thence he went to Belyer [Belper] & there he hath pullyd & rent apon xl [40] houses; and from thence he went to Belper wood and he hathe pullyd downe a wonderous thyng of wood & kylled many bease; & from thens to Brege [Heage] & there hath he pulled downe the chappyl & the moste parte of the towne.' The 'chappyl' was a reference to the church at Etwall, 6 miles (10km) south-west of Derby, and the 'Devil' was actually a tornado track of some 5 miles (8km) in length.

Following a severe and prolonged frost in early December 1564, the Court of Elizabeth I played football on the ice of the Thames at Westminster on New Year's Eve, which must have been an incredible sight. But the thaw set in, and by 5 January the ice was gone. Further north, the thaw caused great floods and many people drowned, especially in and around Yorkshire. Later, in December 1565, the Thames experienced further tidal flooding, likely storm surge related.

ALL SAINTS' FLOOD

A distinctly stormy period during the first week of October 1570 brought misery to a large section of the east coast from the Humber down to the Straits of Dover. With strong gale-force winds and driving rain, extensive flooding of marshland, accentuated by a high tide, was experienced in Maldon and Rainham in Essex. The October storm was short-lived and conditions settled for a few weeks in the run-up to November, when the 'greatest North Sea flood since October 1250' became infamously known as the 'All Saints' Flood'.

The disaster struck the Netherlands, with large loss of life, and there were accounts of a high number of flood-related fatalities in Denmark, Belgium and Germany. Researchers at the Deltawerken Foundation (2004) classified this as the worst disaster in pre-modern times, given that the flood water rose higher than in 1953. On the morning of the floods, the 'Domeinraad' (Domain council) in Bergen op Zoom issued a flood warning for an 'extremely high flood', but sadly the warning had little effect. As dykes collapsed, the coast was inundated between Flanders and Groningen, and also along the north-west of Germany. Antwerp, Friesland and Zeeland were severely flooded. In a letter to King Philip II, the Duke of Alfa stated that no less than five-sixths of the Netherlands was under water. The exact number of casualties is not known, but there is no doubt that the number exceeded 3,000 in the Netherlands. Tens of thousands of people were made homeless, and livestock and winter supplies were destroyed, which led to famine and further fatalities during the winter of 1570/1.

A North Sea windstorm during October 1571 not only destroyed many houses but induced severe coastal flooding along the east coast. Between Lincolnshire and Kent, many ships were wrecked, bridges washed away and cattle drowned. On the 5th near Grimsby, some 20,000 cattle and sheep were caught in the flood waters and reported drowned.

There was some very heavy snow during February 1579, particularly in London. It snowed continuously between the 4th and the 8th, and then hard frosts followed until the 10th. The real problems started with the thaw, which caused high, fast-flowing, ice-filled rivers. These led to floods in many areas, including central London, where Westminster Hall was flooded and fish were left behind in the wake of the flood water. During March, the English Bridge at Shrewsbury suffered, along with some of the surrounding riverside shops. In one incident, a tree trunk thundered down the river, struck the weak props that supported the projecting old buildings, and caused some of them to collapse (Ward, 1935).

EARTHQUAKE IN THE ENGLISH CHANNEL

William Shakespeare's *Romeo and Juliet* mentioned, ''Tis since the earthquake now eleven years,' a reference to events on 6 April 1580 which triggered a tsunami-like event that inundated Dover, Boulogne and Calais, leading to hundreds of fatalities. It is difficult to say exactly whether a tsunami was generated, as distortions in the evidence by sixteenth-century writers could easily have merged seismic activity with other close storm and flood events, but nevertheless the accounts of the earthquake are staggering. In Broadstairs and Sandwich, Kent, inhabitants reported hearing a loud noise that seemed to come from somewhere out in the Channel. Ogley *et al.* (2000) noted, 'There was heard from the southwest a marvellouse greate noyse, as in the twingling of an eye the same noyse was a though yt had been round about the hearers; and therwith began a most fierce and terrible earthquake.'

Harris *et al.* (1996) suggested that the earthquake produced a great sea swell that 'arose in the Channel sinking twenty to thirty British, French and Flemish vessels [with a further fifteen near to Mont St Michel]. A passenger on a boat from Dover reported that his vessel had touched the seabed five times and that the sea had risen into the air more than 50 feet [15m] higher than his vessel.' A study undertaken during the design of the Channel Tunnel suggested that this was one of England's largest earthquakes with an estimated magnitude of 5.3 to 5.9 on the Richter scale and an epicentre beneath the English Channel. It would seem plausible that any seismic shock of this scale would cause some disturbance of the waters, and even tsunami waves, although this is still debated (Melville *et al.*, 1996); indeed 'the sea foamed and ships tottered' was one apt description of events.

As a result of the earthquake, sections of wall fell at Dover Castle as parts of the cliff were lost. A gable-end fell from the north wing of St Peter's church at Broadstairs, and four arches cracked in St Mary's church, Sandwich. Meanwhile, in London, a pinnacle on Westminster Abbey was damaged and falling debris from Christ Church in Newgate caused two fatalities (the first-reported victims of a British earthquake). Across the Channel in Calais, the tremors lasted for about a quarter of an hour, with damage caused by both the earthquake and alleged inundation of water, which engulfed the town and surrounding countryside. Several people and a large number of cattle drowned. Part of the town wall and several houses collapsed. Boulogne was reported to have been flooded and, as buildings shook like leaves, 'wine casks rolled off their stands, furniture was overturned and tables were lifted into the air'. The belfry of Notre-Dame-de Lorette and several buildings at Lille were damaged. Stones and copings fell from buildings in Arras, Douai and Bethune. Several people were killed and injured by falling chimneys and ridge tiles at Oudenaarde in Flanders. Peasants working in the fields reported hearing a loud rumbling noise moving from west to east and saw the ground roll in three or four successive waves.

In 2005, the Department for Environment, Food and Rural Affairs (Defra) published a study, *The Threat Posed by Tsunami to the UK*, which stated, 'On balance, it is most likely that the 1580 earthquake did not cause a tsunami.' What is more interesting is that some geologists believe that the English Channel is well overdue for another tremor. Only time will tell.

THE ROAR OF THE TEMPEST

A 'severe tempest' occurred in the mid-Wye Valley, Herefordshire, during 1585 and was recounted in the *Journal of Meteorology* after some careful and detailed transcription of a rare document discovered by Fairs (1982, p. 187) in Chicago, Illinois: 'A most rare & true report, of such great tempest, strange sightes, and wonderful accidents which happened by the providence of God, in Herefordshire, at a place called the Hay, and thereabouts, besides the sightes of straunge Fowles, which there were seen, most fearful to beholde, with their horrible cryes & strungeness, with the great hurt was done by them.' The account not only gave an insight into the flooding that occurred as a result of the localised thunderstorm but also suggested that a tornado influenced events. An extract of the account with the spelling and punctuation of the original makes fascinating reading (Fairs, 1982, p. 188; reproduced with kind permission of the *International Journal of Meteorology*):

On Saturday being 25 of September past at the Hay in Herefordshire was seen so rare a sight as neither our forefathers have knowne, nor we ourselves heard of. For there rose sodente a most wonderfull and cruell tempeste, with such abundant high waters that the whole countrie was not only greatly amazed therewith, but also in danger of drowning: besides the losse of great and plenteous store of Corne and Cattel, wherewith they were endued: at which instant there appeared a most wonderfull and dreadfull sight of two great cloudes, the one being black, which arising issued from the North, the other being white, came from the South part, which meeting together seemed, to rend the Skie with their ratling, in such unusual sort, that it brought a most rare and terrible terror to the beholders. In the middest of which doutless, opposite with the earth did visibly appear, there situated a faire greene ffield as it had been of fierne, in which field dispersed was seen flying an innumerable companie of black

The fearsome skyscape at
Hay-on-Wye, Herefordshire, on
25 September 1585.
(© *Chris Chatfield*)

Crowes and other Fowles which continuing a certaine time, sent forth most dreadfull straunge and wonderfull cryes, no lesser are to be recited than lamentable to regard: being in altitude to the judgement of the beholders not above 30 fathoms from the earth: with a verye obscene and darke continuance: and not long before the vanishing of these cloudes, was heard so rare and horrible roaring [as if it had been] the cryes of beares and lyons: yea and that so terrible that it was rather judged to have been the skritching of some malevolent hellish and furious fiends: these supposed Crowes were of divers credible persons visibly seen to rent and tear whole houses, barnes and stables, ye and to pull out whole huge trees by the rootes, in a most rare and wonderfull manner, ransacked and dispersed into diverse places: yea and a most dreadful sight some of the rafters and peeces thereof, were carried up in the aire, and after that never sithens seene, with great store of corne which at that time was carried away.

BATTLE OF PINKIE CLEUGH

The Rivers Esk and Tyne have been highly influential rivers, particularly with regard to key battles in Scotland. The Battle of Pinkie Cleugh, fought along the banks of the River Esk near Musselburgh on 10 September 1547, was the first 'modern' battle to be fought in the British Isles. It was historically significant and deemed 'modern' through its demonstration of active cooperation between the infantry, artillery and cavalry, with a naval bombardment in support of the land forces.

The Scots had rejected a proposal for a marriage between Edward, the young king of England, and the infant Mary Queen of Scots (an event known as the 'rough wooing'), and so the Scots formed an alliance with France (Cannon, 2002 edn). An English army led by the Duke of Somerset, protector for Edward VI, against the odds, terrain and weather conditions were victorious over the Scots at Pinkie Cleugh, near Edinburgh. The Scots, led by James Hamilton, second Earl of Arran, and George Gordon, fourth Earl of Huntly, had a numerical advantage but fatally misinterpreted an English retreating manoeuvre. When the two sides met at Pinkie Cleugh, Hamilton ordered his men across the river in a full-out charge, and in doing so lost his advantage. Somerset capitalised on this serious blunder with the use of his artillery. It was a catastrophic defeat for the Scots and was to be known thereafter as 'Black Saturday'. The River Tyne, east of Edinburgh near Haddington, runs to the sea at Tyninghame. Law *et al.* (2005) suggested that on 13 September 1594 English reinforcements moving north to relieve the garrison at Haddington could not do so because the Tyne was in flood, 'as the lyke hath byn syldom se'.

The winter of 1594/5 was particularly severe, with long-drawn-out snow and frosts considered 'black and bitter'. The Berkshire diarist Sidney Gilliham wrote a detailed account of the widespread cold and subsequent flooding that ensued in the spring of 1595 as the thaw set in (Currie *et al.*, 1994). 'My father took me walking . . . and showed me the bodies of beggars frozen to death besides the road. The dead bodies of birds fell from trees and foxes abandoned their wily ways and come into houses to be fed.' During April, the thaw commenced and the severe flooding of the River Thames 'took with it a great toll of life, both human and cattle and it is said that more than 100 were drowned [and] a hundred more died of maladies brought by the waters'. This was just the start of what were to be many winters of discontent.

Chapter 8

THE SEVENTEENTH CENTURY

Behold the wonder of this present age,
A famous river now becomes a stage,
Question not what I now declare to you,
The Thames is now both fair and market too.
And many Thousands dayly do resort,
There to behold the Pastime and the Sport
Early and late, used by young and old,
And valu'd not the fierceness of the Cold.

(Anon., 1684)

The seventeenth century was notable for its severe winters and occasional hot, rainless summers, some of which led to widespread droughts, especially in 1666, the year famous for the Great Fire of London. It was the severe winters and frozen waters, rather than flooded ones, that created much interest this century. The cold climate of the seventeenth century was summarised by Brazell (1968) in his chronology and notes of *London Weather* (*see* Table 2).

The table suggests that 1698 was the coldest year between 1695 and 1742, with frequent heavy frost, hail and snow between January and May. After a deep snow over England on 3 May 1698, the spring was labelled 'the most backward for the past 47 years'. It is not known whether 6 February 1665 really did produce the coldest ever day in England and this information is most likely based on personal diaries at the time. For example, Samuel Pepys (*The Diary of Samuel Pepys*, 1904 edn) recorded on 6 February 1665:

Table 2. *London's weather, 1607–98*

1607/08	Severe frost mid-December to early February; frost fair held on the River Thames.
1609/10	Great frost in October, lasting four months; River Thames frozen, heavy carriages driven over it.
1620/21	Frost fair on the River Thames.
1635	Severe winter; River Thames frozen.
1648/49	Great frost; River Thames frozen.
1658	Very cold winter; snow cover most of the time.
1662/63	Severe frost; River Thames frozen, skating introduced.
1664/65	Severe frost; 6 February 1665 reputed to be one of the coldest days ever in England.
1666/67	Cold winter; hard frost in London on 31 December; River Thames covered with ice on 1 January.
1669	Much colder than 1665 or 1666.
1677	River Thames frozen; huts sell brandy on the river.
1680/81	Severe winter.
1683/84	Severe winter; River Thames frozen from beginning of December to February; longest frost on record; frost fair on the river in the second half of January.
1688/89	Great frost from 20 December to 6 February; frost fair on Thames.
1691/92	Severe winter.
1692	Cold year.
1694/95	Severe winter; frost lasted seven weeks.
1695	One of the coldest years ever known.
1696	Intense frost on 26 January.
1696/97	Severe winter.
1697/98	Severe winter.
1698	Reputed to be the coldest year between 1695 and 1742.

Source: based on selected events from Brazell (1968), Appendix 1: 'Cold weather, snow and frost'.

So home to supper and to bed. This being one of the coldest days, all say, they ever felt in England; and I this day, under great apprehensions of getting an ague from my putting a suit on that hath lain by without ayring a great while, and I pray God it do not do me hurte.

As with any sporadic periods of severe cold, frost, snow and ice, the thaw is inevitable. This can lead to extensive flooding; instances of these throughout the sixteenth century are too numerous to mention, but some of the most notable are summarised within this chapter.

BRISTOL CHANNEL TSUNAMI

The seventeenth century produced great 'non-cold-related' floods, one of the most interesting occurring on 20 January 1606 (quoted as 30 January 1607 in some sources, based on the new-style calendar convention). It has been suggested that this was perhaps a tsunami wave event, as the sudden and unexpected arrival of water covered the tops of houses and pushed up the coast of Somerset 20 miles (32km), and in places inland up to 14 miles (23km), with flood depths recorded at around 12ft (3.6m). The banks on both sides of the River Severn from Bristol to Gloucester were flooded for a staggering 6 miles (10km). The event is recorded on plaques in a number of churches, including those at Kingston Seymour in Somerset, and in Monmouthshire at Goldcliff, St Brides, Redwick and Peterstone. The plaque at Kingston Seymour reads:

> Jan. 20th 1606 . . . an inundation of the sea water by overflowing and breaking down the sea banks happ'd in the Parish of Kingstone-Seamore and many others adjoining by reason whereof many persons were drowned and much cattle and goods were lost, the water in the church was 5 feet high and the greater part lay on the ground for 10 days.

West (2005) made reference to a highly interesting quotation accredited to John Paul, the Vicar of Almondsbury on 26 January 1606. It suggested that 'the river of Severn rose upon a sudden Tuesday morning the 20th of January being the full prime day and highest tide after the change of the moon by reason of a mighty strong western wind. So that from Minehead to Slimbridge the low ground along the river Severn were that turning tide overflown, and in Saltmarsh many houses overthrown, sundry Christians drowned, hundreds of rudder cattle [horned livestock, usually oxen] and horses perished, and thousands of sheep and lambs lost. Unspeakable was the spoil and loss on both sides the river.'

The exact cause of this flood is still debated; Brooks and Glasspoole (1928) suggested that it was due to an unusually high spring tide encountering heavy run-off in the River Severn, a situation that 'may result in the formation of a true "tidal wave".' Conditions very similar to a tidal bore are created when meteorological extremes out at sea amplify high tidal peaks. Laughton and Heddon (1927, p. 6–7) quoted a graphic account of events in their text *Great Storms* that highlighted a more dramatic event hinting towards what we know today as a tsunami:

> . . . huge and mighty hills of water were seen tumbling over one another as if the greatest mountains in the world had overwhelmed the lowest valleys, to the astonishment and terror of the spectators, who at first, mistaking it for a great mist or fog, did not seek to make their escape from it. But on its nearer approach, which seemed faster than the birds could fly they saw that it was the violence of the waters which seemed to have broken bounds, and were pouring in to deluge the whole land. So swift were they that in less than five hours most parts of the counties on Severn banks were under water and many hundreds of persons drowned. From the hills could be seen herds and flocks with husbandmen in the fields all swept away together in one dreadful inundation.

A towering wave rushes up the Bristol Channel on 20 January 1606. (© *Chris Chatfield*)

Contemporary investigations indicate that this was a tsunami wave, as an earth tremor was felt on the morning in question. Researchers suggest that the tsunami, which drove up the Bristol Channel and surrounding areas, was most likely caused by an active fault system off the shore of southern Ireland (Bryant and Haslett, 2002). This fault is known to have caused tremors in the past (a magnitude 4.5 earthquake in 1980). Although, as yet, these have not been large enough to cause a tsunami, it certainly indicates the potential for greater activity. One thing is known: whatever the exact cause of the sudden inundation, it led to a large loss of life, which some put at around 2,000. Among the victims were the family of John Good, who lost his wife, five children and nine servants but managed to save himself by clinging to thatch that carried him for more than a mile before he washed up on a bank. At Bridgwater in Somerset, the market town and two neighbouring villages were flooded by the wave and a reported 500 people drowned, including many sheep and cattle. Other accounts of survival are slightly more colourful, including one of a blind and bedridden man who floated out of his wrecked cottage, and another report of a milkmaid who was marooned for two days on a hill before being rescued 'half dead with fear rather than hunger and cold; for the bank on which she stood was so covered with wild beasts and vermin, which had taken refuge there, that she could scarcely keep them from crawling on her'.

A FEARFUL INUNDATION

Brierley (1964, p. 169) outlined how in Devon on 13 October 1625, 'A tremendous flood swept through the [Exe] valley, causing great devastation. In the town of Tiverton alone 53 houses were destroyed.' Chambers (1874, 1625–1637, Part A) presented a very detailed account of flooding in and around Dumfriesshire on 6 November 1627. The 'tempest of extraordinary violence' not only perilously floated a child's cradle to imminent disaster but destroyed merchant ships and many lives:

At one part of the coast of Scotland, a high tide, assisted by the storm, produced an inundation over a large tract of low land. It came upon the Blackshaw in Carlaverock parish, and upon certain parts of the parish of Ruthwell in such a fearful manner as none then living had ever seen the like. It went at least half a mile beyond the ordinary course, and threw down a number of houses and bulwarks in its way, and many cattle and other bestial were swept away with its rapidity; and, what was still more melancholy, of the poor people who lived by making salt on Ruthwell sands seventeen perished; thirteen of these were found next day, and were all buried together in the churchyard of Ruthwell, which no doubt was an affecting sight to their relations, widows, and children, &c., and even to all that beheld it. One circumstance more ought not to be omitted. The house of Old Cockpool being environed on all hands, the people fled to the top of it for safety; and. so sudden was the inundation upon them, that, in their confusion, they left a young child in a cradle exposed to the flood, which very speedily carried away the cradle; nor could the tenderhearted beholders save the child's life without the manifest danger of their own. But, by the good providence of God, as the cradle, now afloat, was going forth of the Outer door, a corner of it struck against the door-post, by which the other end was turned about; and, going across the door, it stuck there till the waters were assuaged.

Upon the whole, that inundation made a most surprising devastation in those parts; and the ruin occasioned by it had an agreeable influence on the surviving inhabitants, convincing them, more than ever, of what they owed to divine Providence; and for ten years thereafter they had the holy communion about that time, and thereby called to mind even that bodily deliverance.

The Arlingham Parish Register, Gloucestershire, described two events: one on 4 November 1628 in a memorandum titled 'Flood over ½ yard high in Vicarage Barn', and another on 3 February 1629 when it 'ranne not into Vicarage' (Flight, 2004). The vicar of Arlingham wrote:

> Thrice have I seen a fearful inundation
> Within the space of two and twentie years,
> As few of my coate have in all their station;
> Which when it comes (as't will) unto men's eares
> What hart so hard that can abstain from teares?
> But woe is mee that I am first to dwell

> Where seas, enradge with windes, so proudlie swelle!
> God knows who shall survive to see the next,
> To be, as I have binne, with feare perplext.

A windstorm was recorded in Oxfordshire on 11 October 1634 that felled many trees and lifted thatched roofs. This was nothing compared to what surged down the North Sea towards the Netherlands, north-west Germany and Denmark. During the night of the 11th into the 12th a powerful flood, driven by the strong wind, swept away villages, hamlets and even islands. The power of the water destroyed around 50 miles of the coast between Nordstrand island and the Danish border, and resulted in the death of more than 6,000 people. In total, this event was thought to have claimed some 15,000 lives. At Eiderstedt, an area south of Nordstrand, over 2,000 drowned despite being protected by dykes some 18–20ft high (5–6m). Inside the church at Klixbüll, Denmark, locals marked the flood level on the wall, 14ft (4.2m) above ground level.

SUMMERS OF DISCONTENT

The summer of 1648 was very wet, particularly in the south, and well documented on the Isle of Wight during 'the summer of the King being here', which implied the period when King Charles I was held prisoner in Carisbrooke Castle prior to his execution in London (Davison *et al.*, 1993, p. 5):

> The Sommer of the Kinges beinge here 1648: wase more like the winter than Sommer, for his Matie asked me wheather that weather wase usual in our Island. I tolde him this 40 years I have never knew the like before, wee had scarse 3 drie dayes togeather but rayne hygh windes & stormes. In Awgust we had not one drye daye, so that the corne wase like to rotte in ye ground.

July 1662 produced a thunderstorm so severe that it was said to signal 'the day of judgment' at Ormskirk, Lancashire. Flooding, was not the main problem this time; rather, it was the enormous hailstones. The Revd Nathaniel Heywood, Vicar of Ormskirk, wrote, 'Hailstones were as big as ordinary apples, some say nine inches compass; one stone that I took up was about four inches after it had thawed in my hand.' The storm naturally caused much damage to property and crops: 'The hail broke all our glass windows westward, we have not one quarrel [a pane of glass, often rhomboid or diamond-shaped] whole on that side; and so it is with most of the houses in and about the town. It hath cut off all the ears of our standing corn, so that most fields that were full of excellent barley and other grain are not worth reaping. . . . all, especially the ignorant, were much terrified, thinking it had been the day of judgment.'

Thunderstorms and associated flooding were a focus in 1663. Samuel Pepys made the following diary entry for 5 May 1663: 'About 11 at night going to bed it fell a-thundering and lightening [*sic*], the greatest flashes enlightening the whole body of the yard, that ever I saw in my life.' Then, on the 15th, he wrote:

Strange were the effects of the late thunder and lightning about a week since at Northampton, coming with great rain, which caused extraordinary floods in a few hours, bearing away bridges, drowning horses, men, and cattle. Two men passing over a bridge on horseback, the arches before and behind them were borne away, and that left which they were upon: but, however, one of the horses fell over, and was drowned.

Pepys is referring to the flash flood at Northampton on 6 May, when the high raging torrents of flood water forced away two arches of the South Bridge. Other sources mentioned 'great rains' and 'a prodigious flood' on 7 May further south of Northampton and around Oxford; it would seem that these are the same storms described by Pepys. The end of the year produced one of the highest tidal floods on record in London on 7 December 1663. The flood, driven by gales, submerged Whitehall as the tide rose to over 16ft (4.9m) above the present ordnance datum. This was probably the effects of a storm surge, as there were further impacts along the Thames estuary and North Sea coast.

The spring and summer of 1666 were very dry and warm. Many waited for the rains to come but these were few and far between. There was some relief from the drought in July and an entry in the diary of Samuel Pepys for 16 July noted, 'A wonderful dark sky, and shower of rain this morning, which at Harwich proved so too with a shower of hail as big as walnuts.' It was not long before the cold returned and the Revd Thomas Mossley, rector of Darley Dale, Derbyshire, wrote about a great frost which began at Martinmas 1676 and continued until 3 January 1677: 'Ye Derwent was actually frozen, and att ye dissolving of the frost a great flood, and incredible quantities of ice was brought out on the water banks into tollerable inclosed grounds and up to the churchyard steps.'

April into May 1682 was very wet; on 22 April the diary of John Evelyn recorded the spring season as 'unusually wet, with rain and thunder'. This was supported by the Revd William Sampson, rector of Clayworth, Nottingham, who went further, suggesting instances of flooding as a result. The Revd Sampson started *The Rector's Book of Clayworth, Nottingham*, which included numerous personal, parochial and diocesan entries from 27 March 1676 to the end of 1701. In 1682 he wrote, 'Fro' ye middle of April to ye middle of May it was very wett: the meadows were generally drowned' (Sampson, 1910 edn). Worse was to come in London, where flooding from the River Thames did substantial damage in and around Brentford. The following quotation later appeared in *The Times* on 16 January 1928: 'Never was such flodds known as has bine here, howses drowned and pore children drowne in theare cradels swimen up Fleet Bridge, and there taken up, and tables and hogeds full of beare and all washed away, and peoppele getting up to theare uper lofts and hole heards of hogs drowned.'

FROST FAIRS AND FLOODS

It may seem a contrast to discuss rivers that are more often known for their flooding being frozen, static and lifeless, especially the grand River Thames. One of the first reports of the Thames being completely frozen was during the severe winter of 1149/50. The ice was so thick that Londoners were able to cross the river on foot and horseback. Another instance occurred during the winter of 1204/05. Some twenty-three winters produced similar conditions between 1260 and 1814, with eight well-documented frost fairs held on the Thames between 1607 and 1814.

Evidently, these cold spells produced a somewhat more lively environment than might have been expected. The most famous of the fairs was staged during the winter of 1683/4, when the frost lasted from early December to early February (although the fair was confined to late January 1684). Shops and booths covered the ice, resembling formal streets. They sold a variety of merchandise and even incorporated trades, including a printing press. The practice by visitors to the press of having their names printed together with the date and the phrase 'printed on the Thames' became so popular that the printer became an entrepreneur overnight. A picture and poem of the frost fair printed by Haly and Millet in 1684 recounted what seems an unbelievable practice in comparison to today's climate:

> Before the Temple there a Street is made,
> And there is one almost of every Trade,
> There may you also this hard Frosty Winter,
> See on the Rocky Ice a Working-PRINTER,
> Who hopes by his own Art to reap some gain,
> Which he perchance does think he may obtain.

The Diary of John Evelyn (1996, vol. 3, p. 120–1) also noted the severity of the frost this winter, along with the 'ice printer's' business acumen:

24th. The frost continuing more and more severe. The Thames before London was still planted with booths in formal streets, all sorts of trades and shops furnished, and full of commodities, even to a printing press, where the people and ladies took a fancy to have their names printed, and the day and year set down when printed on the Thames: this humour took so universally, that it was estimated the printer gained £5 a day, for printing a line only, at sixpence a name, besides what he got by ballads, etc.

Drawings of the frost fairs showed the variety of activities that went on. There was dancing, and sports like football, skating, wrestling, skittles and sledging, along with other pastimes including bull-baiting, bear-baiting and fox-hunting. Gambling was also rife, with horse and coach races taking place up and down the frozen river. The ice was so thick that even an ox was roasted. It should be borne in mind, however, that although the often colourful prose and descriptions of the frost fairs depict a level of prosperity,

A sharp contrast: the River Thames completely frozen and not flooded. Taken from *Great Britain's Wonder: or, London's Admiration . . . the Wonder of this present Age, and a great consternation to all the Spectators*, printed in London by M. Haly and J. Millet, and sold by 'Robert Walton, at the Globe on the North-side of St Pauls-Church, near that end towards Ludgate. . . . And by John Seller in the West-side of the Royal Exchange', 1684. *(Courtesy www.she-philosopher.com)*

this by no means matched the level of misery that the severe frosts produced. With watercourses totally frozen, those with livelihoods reliant on the water, like dockers, watermen, boatmen and fishermen, were naturally unemployed. The severe cold meant that anyone who worked outside suffered great hardship, and fuel and food supplies were in very short supply.

Money (1905, p. 75), in his text *A Popular History of Newbury*, summarised well the privations inflicted by the extreme cold around the end of the seventeenth century, and it is no surprise that the flood waters were soon to return as a result of the thaw:

The frost this year was terrible. It began in the beginning of December, 1683; there was then a constant frost for seven weeks, producing ice eighteen inches thick. Many parks of deer were destroyed, and flocks of sheep, the forest trees, and even the oaks were split by the frost; most of the hollies were killed, and nearly all the birds perished. The Kennet was froze over, and when the thaw came the greater part of the town [Newbury] was flooded; the town bridge was considerably damaged, and had to be temporarily secured by shores and props, while the neighbouring Marsh Bridge was bodily carried away, and landed in a neighbouring meadow. The flood of waters made a breach in the river bank at the bridge and in other places, so that great fears were entertained that the whole town would be inundated, but this was happily averted by the prompt measures taken.

The harsh, frozen winters of the seventeenth century, followed by thaw and floods, certainly left their mark on the landscape and the lives of many. Those who had suffered and survived hoped for a more temperate climate in the eighteenth century; but, as the century drew to a close, who would have believed that one of the greatest storms ever was about to occur?

Chapter 9

THE EIGHTEENTH CENTURY

... it was a catastrophic tempest, followed by a prodigious tide.

(The Revd William Derham)

The eighteenth century produced what is considered one of the worst windstorms to have occurred in Britain, with the loss of some 8,000 lives on land and sea over 26 and 27 November 1703. Much was written at the time, and has been since, about this storm. The most detailed account came from Daniel Defoe (1704), who toured the counties to assess the damage (he is quoted as having counted some 17,000 fallen trees before tiring of the immense task) and invited correspondence from all parts of the country for his report, *A wonderful history of all the storms, hurricanes, earthquakes, &c. that have happen'd in England for above 500 years past . . . with a particular and large account of the dreadful storm, that happen'd on the 26th and 27th of November, 1703, etc.*

One of the contributors was the Revd William Derham (1657–1735), a keen weather observer and writer. Some of his earliest letters contained detailed observations of the weather in Upminster, Essex. He went on to become chaplain to the Prince of Wales (1716) and then Canon of Windsor (1730), and is also famous for editing the works of John Ray (one of the most eminent naturalists of his time) and Robert Hooke (philosopher, inventor, surveyor and architect). He also contributed to Daniel Defoe's history of the storm of 1703. William Derham wrote about the storm in and around London, particularly the interactions between wind and tides and the implications for flooding (Brooks and Glasspoole, 1928, p. 88):

Another unhappy circumstance with which this disaster was join'd was a prodigious tide, which happen'd the next day but one, and was occasion'd by the fury of the winds; which is also a demonstration, that the winds veer'd for part of the time to the northward; and as it is observable, and known by all that understand our sea affairs, that a North West Wind makes the Highest Tide, so this blowing to the Northward, and that with such unusual violence, brought up the sea raging in such a manner that in some parts of England 'twas incredible, the water rising 6 or 8 foot higher than it was ever known to do in the memory of man.

This is an interesting early assessment of tidal flooding. Comparisons and extensions of Derham's observations were drawn by Brooks and Glasspoole (1928) in their discussion of 'the great flood of the 2nd January 1877', in which they suggested an added complication. During such events, the power of a strong east wind drives the water of a rising tide into the narrowing estuary of the Thames, amplifying the height of the water. They also discussed the role played by the relationship between the sun and moon in influencing tides, and the effect of atmospheric pressure in amplifying the sea state.

The 1703 storm was caused by a series of low-pressure systems that intensified to produce extremely severe wind speeds over 100mph (87 knots), the equivalent of at least a category 2 hurricane (96–110mph, 83–96 knots, based on the Saffir-Simpson hurricane scale). The windstorm drove a massive storm surge into the Severn estuary, flooding villages along the north Somerset coast as well as the centre of Bristol. It is interesting to read Laughton and Heddon's (1927) interpretation of events, which suggested that at Bristol the water was 8ft (2.4m) above the highest recorded level; indeed, 'at Chepstow they had long memories, and it was a question whether a flood of 1607 (1606, old style) had not been as high or even higher'. The issue of whether or not this was the case does not detract from the fact that at least £100,000 worth of damage (approximately £12 million, based on a 2004 conversion) was done at Bristol, 'a great part of it from the flooding of cellars in which was stored the rich produce of the West Indies and America: 1,000 hogsheads of sugar [and] 1,500 of tobacco . . . are enumerated among the losses'. Indeed, it seemed the loss was far greater: 'They tell us,' said Defoe, 'the damage done by the tide amounts to above £200,000 [approximately

£24 million at 2004 prices]; 15,000 sheep drown'd in one level, multitudes of cattle on all the sides, and the covering of lands with salt water is a damage cannot well be estimated.'

The salt content of the storm had an interesting and widespread effect. A report in *Symons's Monthly Meteorological Magazine* (1872) recounted a letter from a John Fuller of Sussex (dated 6 December 1703 and previously published in *Philosophical Transactions*, 1704), who noted the unusual effects of the sea salt that had been carried within the driving wind and rain and was later found on trees some 25 miles (40km) from the coast: 'We live 10 miles off the sea in a direct line . . . but [it was evident] that the sea-water was blown thus far, [since] all the twigs of the trees the day after were white, and tasted very salty.' Similarly, Laughton and Heddon (1927) wrote in their analysis, 'a curious result of the storm, it was noticed in the Isle of Wight that the fine spray of the sea, blown many miles inland, had rendered the grass so salty that cattle could not eat; and that hedges and trees showed on the ends of their twigs knobs of salt congealed. The same thing appeared in Sussex and Kent, especially at Cranbook.' It was suggested that this is a regular feature of West Indian hurricanes, but unprecedented in England. This is not necessarily the case. The county-based Dorset Coastal Storms Database discussed by Doe (2002) highlighted at least two other occurrences relating to coastal storms and saline transportation. On 29 April 1882 along the Dorset coast, 'A peculiar effect of the storm was that a great portion of the foliage exposed to its assaults had been reduced to a shrivelled state, as if by the action of fire. The distance to which the sea brine may have been carried inland by a heavy tempest has been known to exceed 30 miles.' Then, on 2 June 1938, 'As a result of the 80 mph gale miles of hawthorn hedge were blackened and sycamores were turned a hideous yellow clay colour up to 5 miles inland by the salt encrusted gale.'

Along the English Channel coast the wind raged at full strength for over eight hours overnight on 27 into 28 November 1703, producing a Channel storm surge that, combined with powerful wave action, devastated the then village of Brighthelmstone (now known as Brighton). Defoe (1704) wrote, 'Brighthelmstone being an old-built and poor, though populous, town was miserably torn to pieces and made the very picture of desolation that it look't as if an enemy had sack't it.' Worse still, the Channel squadron, commanded

The Great Storm of 1703, 'Wherein Rear Admiral Beaumont was lost on the Goodwin Sands'. *(Courtesy National Maritime Museum)*

at the time by Rear Admiral Sir Basil Beaumont, was entirely lost. As the storm abated, it was said that as many as 1,000 survivors from the ships that had been washed on to the Goodwin Sands during the night were alive on the sands offshore. It was controversially recorded by Daniel Defoe that the assistance of townsmen at nearby Deal, Kent was sought but that they ignored the request because 'the pickings from the sea were so good at the time.' Anyone who had made it on to the sands that night died. After the incident, Defoe wrote a disparaging ode (BBC, 2005):

> If I had any satire left to write,
> Could I with suited spleen indite,
> My verse should blast that fatal town,
> And drown'd sailors' widows pull it down;
> No footsteps of it should appear,

And ships no more cast anchor there.
The barbarous hated name of Deal shou'd die,
Or be a term of infamy;
And till that's done, the town will stand
A just reproach to all the land.

HIGH TIDES AND HEAVY RAIN

Recovery was very slow after the great storm of 1703, especially along the south coast. A summer south-westerly storm on 11 August 1705 brought a costly reminder to those still in vulnerable coastal fringes. At Brighton, the lower fronting parts of the town became covered by an enormous bank of shingle that was deposited by the powerful wind-driven waves.

Further west towards Dorset on 16 May 1709 a severe thunderstorm lasted three hours at Sherborne Abbey, in what was described as 'a Great Hailstorme' (some hailstones were recorded at 6in, or 15cm, in circumference). This was accompanied by intense rainfall, which caused a small river next to the abbey to burst its banks and inundate the grounds with such force that the torrents forced open the north door, removing over 1,000ft (300m) of pavement and displacing seats in its wake. An inscription in the abbey records the flood waters as 2ft 10in (0.9m) high.

The floods of Christmas 1717 are still spoken of in northern Europe today, as a result of the scale of the loss of life along the coasts of the Netherlands, Germany and Scandinavia inflicted by a severe storm surge. Researchers at Deltawerken Foundation (2004) estimated that around 14,000 lost their lives, with the low-lying Dutch coastline suffering greatly. In the province of Groningen, villages that were situated directly behind the dykes were swept away. Action had to be taken against looters, who robbed houses and farms under the pretence of rescuing the flood victims.

Flooding of the River Nene, the Fens and Wisbech led to comparisons with events from 1703. Law *et al.* (2005) recorded in their database events from the *British Chronologist* (1789 edn), which noted on 8 January 1735:

. . . a terrible storm of wind that did a great deal of mischief both at sea and on shore. . . . About an hour before noon, the wind increased to a storm, at W. and W.S.W. so violent as has not been known since that memorable one November 27, 1703; in comparison of which it was of longer continuance, but some think it not quite so violent . . . The rivers being high from the great rains before, and during the storm, the waters were forced over their banks and overflowed the low lands; sheep and other cattle were lost in some places; in others the people took to their upper rooms to secure themselves from the inundations that were on every side. But we have not room to enumerate more particulars of the damage done before 6 o'clock in the evening, about which time it abated; nor indeed is it necessary; for the effects of it were perceived in much the same manner, at the same time, in every corner of the kingdom, and consequently by all its inhabitants. But we must not omit the good, occasioned by this dreadful tempest, to the harbour of Wisbich, which is deepened by the freshes to above 15 foot water, so that ships come up to the town, which saving lighterage, has been of great service to the trade of that port.

It was thought that 16 February 1736 produced the highest tide for fifty years on the Thames. This high tide also flooded the coastal lowlands of the east coast between Lincolnshire and Kent and resulted in the death of thousands of cattle, along with their owners who tried to save them. Foulness, on the Essex coast, was completely inundated: 'Not a hoof was saved thereon, and inhabitants were taken from the upper part of their houses into boats.'

The *British Chronologist* (1789 edn) recorded a flood from a 'cloudburst' in 1738 over Scholes Moor, Yorkshire, from which 'a prodigious quantity of water descended in cataract form down the ravines and narrow gullies, swelling the larger rivulets into impetuous torrents'. This flood was the result of an intense local thunderstorm on 7 May. Arthur Jessop, an apothecary in New Mill, Huddersfield, kept a detailed diary between 1734 and 1742; his entry for events in May 1738 recorded how Holmfirth chapel was flooded as high as the pews. As the water rushed through the chapel, the congregation were said to have shown 'great consternation and alarm'.

Reynolds (1991, p. 305) discussed the previously unpublished weather records from the diary of Dr Richard Wilkes. Wilkes's diary noted for the

118

period between 8 and 12 December 1740 serious flooding in and around the Shropshire area involving the River Severn. He wrote:

December 8th
There has been a continual flood for more than a fortnight and the snow going away suddenly with the rain on the 8th we had the greatest flood that has been known for many years. I never remember so much rain to have fallen at any time in the same number of days.

December 10th
The Severn was higher on the 10th than it had ever been since the year 1672. As it rose suddenly much damage was done and several persons drowned. At Bridgnorth one of the middle arches of the bridge fell in on the 11th and did much hurt to two houses that the inhabitants were forced to quit them. Tho' the arches are very high the water almost touched the top of the highest and on the 12th I was forced to go by boat to the High Town when the water, tho' falling, covered a piece of ground below the bridge called the Bylet near a yard as we supposed.

Further afield, Wilkes noted on 19 December 1740, 'Prodigious quantities of rain fell not only here but in Holland, France, Germany and almost every country in Europe which by swelling the rivers so as to overflow their banks did prodigious damage. We also had great storms, hurricanes, lightning, thunder and earthquakes in the two months of November and December' (Reynolds, 1991, p. 305).

A STUPENDOUS CLOUDBURST

There was an unsettled start to 1743, and an east coast gale over 23 and 24 February affected Sandwich and Walmer, Kent, with high seas, floods and many ships wrecked; fatalities were inevitable and were reported to be in excess of fifty. By July, summer thunderstorms were to make their mark in many ways. There were reports of hailstones at Enfield as big as nutmegs, which broke windows and severely damaged the corn for several miles around. A boy and two horses were struck dead by lightning during a widespread thunderstorm. At Leicester, pieces of ice reported at around 5in (13cm) in length, and hailstones 2in (5cm) in circumference, killed hundreds of small birds. The thawing of such a fall of ice led to flooded streets, with water several feet deep in many houses.

The summer of 1747 was considered warm and dry, particularly during July and August. However, on 3 June a violent thunderstorm over the South Downs, with an accompanying downpour of heavy rain that lasted for about three hours, led to flash flooding, sweeping away the bridge at Midhurst, Sussex. The River Rother overflowed to such a degree that flooding in the church and churchyard at Midhurst was several feet deep. The floods caused widespread damage to the corn crop, and several sheep were caught unawares and drowned. Tragically, lightning struck two men, who died instantly.

August 1749 produced a flash flood of notable proportions in the parish of St John's, Keswick, Cumberland, particularly in and around Wanthwaite. *British Rainfall* (HMSO, 1931, p. 78) noted a 'most stupendous cloudburst', and Bulman (2001) transcribed extracts from the *History, Gazetteer, and Directory of Cumberland* (Mannix and Whellan, 1847) that described how a:

> . . . waterspout of uncommon dimensions and force broke over this district on the 22nd August 1749, and in less than 2 hours deluged the valley many feet deep, sweeping away all the bridges, walls, houses, and almost completely erasing a corn mill which stood on the banks of the stream. This remarkable fall of water was accompanied with the most terrible thunder and incessant lightning imaginable; and, what seems uncommon, a buzzing noise, like that of a malt kiln, or the sound of the wind in the tops of trees. In the widest part of the dale is a separate broken and rugged rock, called Green Crag, [Castle Rock] which stands threatening the valley, and, to a distant observer, has the appearance of an ancient ruined castle, rising from the summit of a little mount.

EARTHQUAKES AND FLASH FLOODS

In 1750 there was an earthquake near Nottinghamshire thought to be as strong as 4.0 on the Richter scale. Some accounts noted that during the earthquake, dogs howled in unearthly tones and fish jumped out of the River

Trent. There were plenty of thunderstorms that year, with heavy rain and flash floods in July; and at the beginning of August, in Scotland, the *British Chronologist* (1789 edn, p. 68) noted:

There fell, some miles above Altyr [Altyre], in the county of Murray [*sic*], in Scotland, such a quantity of rain, that a small river running by that place, rose 22 feet perpendicular above the common level of the water, and did incredible damage to the fine fields lying along its banks, by initially carrying off some, and covering others with immense quantities of sand and gravel; it swept away with it several houses and mills, and the corn of the whole possessions. As the waters in that neighbourhood rose in no proportion to the burn of Altyr, it is imagined, that what is called a waterspout fell near the source of this small river; as it did in Lorrain on the precise day that this happened at Altyr.

The reference here is to a location near to Altyre, most probably one of the tributaries south of Forres. This was a summer flash flood event and the waterspout referred to is not what the term suggests to us today, but a dense column of localised rain with a very high precipitation rate. The storms lingered in north-east Scotland for a few days, and south-east towards Aberdeen, the River Don rose to such a height that the *British Chronologist* (1789 edn) reported, 'in the middle of the night, it carried off half of a large house, furniture and all. The gentlewoman of the house was providentially abroad, and her youngest son narrowly escaped with his life, the water having surrounded his bed.' A similar storm leading to flash flooding was also noted in the *British Chronologist* at the beginning of September 1750 at Gloucester: it was 'the most violent rain ever known, lasting 3 hours, with very little intermission, by which the principal streets were above 3 feet deep, so that most of the cellars were filled, and many of their shops. At Stroud and Painswick several mills were much damaged, large trees and hedges carried away, and walls thrown down by the torrent; some had thirty ton of coal washed away, others their furnaces carried out of their stacks, and a bridge called Dodbridge was forced up; the damage was computed at several thousand pounds.'

Yorkshire was the focus of events for 1754, an earthquake occurring during the spring, while the autumn produced flash flooding in and around the moors. Late in the evening on 19 April a tremor was felt in York and neighbouring villages. Tremors were also felt in Whitby and Hull, happening in the still of night, which terrified residents. But it was during October 1754 that a number of notable flash floods around the North Yorkshire Moors were reported. Some sources suggest that there were two separate, but equally devastating, events in one week around the 3rd and 10th. Jefferson (1821) in his text *The History of Thirsk* stated that Thirsk bridge was entirely washed away by 'a tremendous inundation, unequalled in the memory of the oldest inhabitants. Great damage was sustained by the inhabitants whose property was situated near the banks of the river.' Law *et al.* (2005) recorded in their database a detailed account of events from the *British Chronologist* (1789 edn):

A sudden inundation of the river Rye happened at Helmsley in Yorkshire, such as had never been known by the oldest people in those parts, probably occasioned by the late heavy rains. Two houses were entirely washed away, the one inhabited by James Holdforth, he and his whole family drowned, except his wife, who being sick in her bed, was carried down the stream half a mile, and at last washed off into a field, where she was found the next morning very little hurt. The other house belonged to John Sunley, was also drowned, and all his family. In the whole thirteen persons. Two other houses were greatly damaged, as was also the stone bridge at the entrance to the town; fourteen hay-stacks were driven down the river a mile, on one of which was a half year old calf, who kept its footing, and was taken off alive. The kitchen-garden walls, and part of those of the park, belonging to the fine seat of Thomas Duncombe esq. were washed away. Two large bridges, one of stone, the other of wood, at Rivaulx, were driven down, as were several more lying upon the river Rye, and others damaged. A malt-kiln, with a large quantity of malt and cinders at Rivaulx, belonging to Robert Berry, were utterly destroyed. The water formed a vent for itself, by forcing through the wall of his kitchen, which prevented the house from being driven down; the man and his family saved their lives by getting up into the chambers. There had also been terrible havoc among the inhabitants at Rivaulx, as well as at Helmsley, by damaging of houses and drowning of cattle. One Simpson, a farmer at Rivaulx, had seven calves drowned; and Robert Sandwith's tanyard at Helmsley, were utterly destroyed, and leather washed out of the pits to a great value. The river Derwent was never known higher in the memory of man. Mr Creasor, of Ferby, near Malton, was drowned near Westow, in his return home from Pocklington fair. Thirsk bridge was entirely washed away, and the inhabitants suffered great damage, but no lives lost.

Members of the Yorkshire Archaeological Society extracted an interesting account of the flood from the diary of John Pape with its original spelling as follows (McDonnell, 1963, p. 464):

October the 28th, 1754: A great and trable flud of water came by the rever Reye to Helmslay blakeymour, which came with such veamancy that it drove to the ground 8 houses, 5 dwelling houses. Thorten poure creaters wear dround besides a great deal of catel, hey and corn staks. It drove down most part of Helmsla Bredg . . . and Revolx bredg down to the ground, and part of Bow bredg and Shacan bredg and abondance of damage in the country besides. . . . A while after a flood came by Borrow Beck, which filed William Ward and John Bentley's selars, and was very ney running down the market place, and water came on Bondgate as beg as Rey Bek.

Earthquake and floods were synonymous with 1755. Floods in the United Kingdom during February, June, July, September and December are worth mentioning, particularly the thunderstorm flash flood event between Cambridge and Bury St Edmunds in June. The storm was reported to have started at around 3 p.m., and two hours later at 5 p.m. the flash flood waters were around 6ft (1.8m) deep, affecting Newmarket and the neighbouring village of Cheveley, where the cloudburst originated. In Newmarket, flood waters overflowed cellars and filled several shops with 2ft (0.6m) of water. The market stalls had to be tied to signposts to prevent their being carried away by the rapid 'flash'. The *British Chronologist* (1789 edn) noted:

. . . the torrent was so immediate, the inhabitants had no time to help themselves; it came with such rapidity that it beat down two people in crossing the street, so that with great difficulty they saved their lives. Its force was so great that it displaced grave-stones in the church-yard, and removed pews in the church. The water was 4 feet deep in several houses, particularly the Star-Inn, where it came in with such strength that if a wall in the yard had not given way, and two men had been placed to hold the gates of the yard open, the whole house must soon have been beaten down; in the cellars twenty-eight hogsheads of beer and two pipes of wine were staved and all lost.

July saw similar thunderstorm-induced flooding of some 5ft (1.5m) at Margate in Kent, while September brought what was described by residents as 'the greatest fall of rain ever known in the north of England', though this may be seen as something of an exaggeration. The sudden swelling of rivers and torrents of flood waters caught many by surprise along the rivers Spey and Findhorn, which rose by some 12ft (3.6m) and carried

A tsunami caused by the Lisbon earthquake engulfed the Portuguese capital on 1 November 1755. (*The Jan T. Kozak Collection, courtesy National Information Service for Earthquake Engineering, University of California, Berkeley*)

away timber, grain and cattle. Small rivulets rose to great heights and a woman and boy drowned in the flood water of the River Dulnain, Strathspey, along with another woman in the waters of the River Lossie, near Elgin.

The best-remembered event of 1755 is the disastrous Lisbon, Portugal earthquake on 1 November. At the time it was one of the most destructive earthquakes in Europe, with fatality figures estimated at between 60,000 and 100,000, as giant tsunami waves flooded Lisbon and surrounding areas. The Revd Charles Davy (1755) witnessed the tsunami and wrote the following account:

> On a sudden I heard a general outcry, 'The sea is coming in, we shall be all lost.' Upon this, turning my eyes towards the river, which in that place is nearly four miles broad, I could perceive it heaving and swelling in the most unaccountable manner, as no wind was stirring. In an instant there appeared, at some small distance, a large body of water, rising as if it were like a mountain. It came on foaming and roaring, and rushed towards the shore with such impetuosity, that we all immediately ran for our lives as fast as possible; many were actually swept away, and the rest above their waist in water at a good distance from the banks.

If we look at this earthquake tsunami event in context, it is clear, especially in comparison with more recent examples, how severe this event really was. At the time of writing, it is listed as the fifteenth most destructive earthquake on record (*see* Table 3).

It is not known whether the earthquake or indeed tsunami had much impact on the United Kingdom. The epicentre was thought to be towards the North African plate and the Eurasian plate, and tremors were felt as far north as Scotland as well as in the south, in Sussex. As a result, some sources note that water in ponds and rivers in the United Kingdom was thrown high into the air and drenched the banks for several feet, leaving fish on dry land. It was thought that some of the waves generated by the earthquake made their way to Mounts Bay in Cornwall. However, by the time they reached the United Kingdom, they had lost most of their

Table 3. *The most destructive known earthquakes on record in the world with 50,000 or more deaths. It is estimated that the Lisbon earthquake was around 8.5–8.7 in magnitude*

Date	Location	Deaths (estimated)	Magnitude (some estimated)	Comments
[23 January 1556	China, Shansi	830,000	~8	
26 December 2004	Sumatra	283,106	9.0	Deaths from earthquake and tsunami
27 July 1976	China, Tangshan	255,000	7.5	Estimated death toll as high as 655,000
9 August 1138	Syria, Aleppo	230,000		
22 May 1927	China, near Xining	200,000	7.9	Large fractures
22 December 856	Iran, Damghan	200,000		
16 December 1920	China, Gansu	200,000	7.8	Major fractures, landslides
23 March 893	Iran, Ardabil	150,000		
1 September 1923	Japan, Kanto Kwanto	143,000	7.9	Great Tokyo fire
5 October 1948	USSR Turkmenistan, Ashgabat	110,000	7.3	
28 December 1908	Italy, Messina	70,000 to 100,000	7.2	Deaths from earthquake and tsunami
September 1290	China, Chihli	100,000		
November 1667	Caucasia, Shemakha	80,000		
18 November 1727	Iran, Tabriz	77,000		
1 November 1755	Portugal, Lisbon	70,000	~8.7	Great tsunami

Source: the data for this table extract are supplied courtesy of the US Geological Survey Earthquake Hazards Program.

destructive power and little damage was recorded. A series of tsunami waves was also triggered west across the Atlantic and noted as far away as the West Indies.

The winter of 1756/7 was a particularly cold one. An abundance of snow on Salisbury Plain and in west Berkshire created, on thawing, a flash flood at Imber and Lambourn. Imber was a small village a few miles south-west of West Lavington on Salisbury Plain and had a population of over 600 in 1831. In 1943 the villagers were required to vacate Imber so that it could be handed over to the army for military training. Prior to this, the village suffered a devastating flash flood from rapid snow-melt towards the end of February 1757, which completely destroyed two cottages. It was described as 'the most remarkable flood known in the memory of man at Imber'. Meanwhile, at Lambourn, just over 35 miles (56km) to the north-west of Imber, a similar flash flood occurred. The *British Chronologist* (1789 edn) noted a sudden thaw as a result of melting snow on neighbouring hills, when water 'came down in such a torrent, that the inhabitants of several houses (that stood most exposed, and which were afterwards washed down) with difficulty saved their lives: a malt-house was borne down, and three floors of malt entirely washed away: a carpenter had seven loads of timber, among which was one piece 55 feet [17m] long, carried by the current some hundred yards from the place where it lay.' Brierley (1964, p. 169) made reference to another remarkable flash flood, also in 1757, caused by heavy overnight rain in Devon; as a result, 'the Exe rose suddenly and swept away the Mill House situated at the end of West Exe, Tiverton. Many bridges were destroyed or damaged throughout the Exe Valley.'

An unusual phenomenon occurred on 31 March 1761, according to the *Annual Register* (1761, p. 92). At around 2 p.m., 'Loch Ness rose on a sudden above 2 feet [0.6m] in perpendicular height, and continued alternately rising and falling, for the space of three quarters of an hour. . . . in the middle of the Loch, the water swelled up like a mountain, and during the whole time appeared extremely muddy and dirty. What makes it still more extraordinary, it was a perfect calm for several hours before and after. The motion was attended with a very uncommon hollow sound.' Was this disturbance caused by the mythical Loch Ness monster? Probably not, as similar water disturbances were observed during the Lisbon earthquake.

THE IRRUPTION OF SOLWAY MOSS

A long spell of particularly wet years started in 1768 and continued until 1775. Brooks and Glasspoole (1928) suggested that there was heavy rainfall and flooding in February 1768; indeed the *Annual Register* (1768, p. 72) noted, 'there was the greatest flood ever known at Hereford: the water came into Wye-bridge-Street as high as the Royal Oak; and on Thursday all the flat country near Ross was overflowed. The causeway between Ross and Wilton was so much under water that several people in returning from Ross market missed the causeway, and must have been drowned if some boats had not fortunately come to their assistance.'

The spring was dry and cold, summer was dismal and the heaviest rains came towards the end of the summer, in September, the *Annual Register* (1768, p. 163) suggesting that 'The heaviest rain fell at London and the country round it that has been known in the memory of man. It began in the evening, and in a few hours the waters poured down Highgate Hill with incredible violence; the common shores in several parts of the town not being able to carry off the torrent, the adjacent houses were filled almost to the first floors; immense damage was done, and as it happened in the night, many were awakened from sleep in the greatest consternation.' The rains and floods continued to be prevalent throughout the autumn and early winter. By December the Thames reached a flood level higher than any in the preceding years, and according to Symons and Chatterton (1895), 'The Kennet and Loddon overflowed their banks. Burfield Bridge and part of Twyford Bridge were washed away and the Isis at Oxford rose 1 feet 6 inches [0.46m] above existing high water mark. The [London to] Exeter coach, with six passengers and four horses, was carried away by the flood near Staines, and all were drowned.'

November 1771 was very unsettled with heavy rain between the 6th and 17th. It was the incessant rains between Friday 16th and the early hours of Sunday 17 November 1771 that produced a dramatic impact on the lives and landscape in and around Carlisle and Newcastle. The *Annual Register* (1771, p. 159) published a letter from a clergyman at Carlisle who described what must have been the most amazing sight, as the flood waters swelled the sphagnum moss on the moors:

I believe that there is nothing so surprising, and were it not well attested, so incredible, as what happened at Solway Moss, which lies on the borders of Scotland, about ten miles north of Carlisle. A great part of this moss (at least 400 acres of it) began to swell by the inundation, and rose to such a height that at last it rolled forward like a torrent, and continued its course above a mile, sweeping along with it houses and trees, and every other thing in its way: it divided itself into islands of different extent from 1 to 10 feet [0.3–3.1m] thickness, upon which were found hares, moor-game.

A more detailed account was published in the *Encyclopaedia Americana* (1883, vol. 13, p. 511), which quoted the testimony of Mr William Gilpin:

On the thirteenth of November, 1771, in a dark, tempestuous night, the inhabitants of the plain were alarmed with a dreadful crash, which they could no way account for: many of them were then in the fields, watching their cattle, lest the Esk, which was then rising violently in the storm, should carry them off [three days' rain, of unusual violence, preceded the irruption]. In the mean time, the enormous mass of fluid substance, which had burst from the moss, moved on slowly, spreading itself more and more as it got possession of the plain. Some of the inhabitants, through the terror of the night, could plainly discover it advancing like a moving hill. This was, in fact, the case; for the gush of mud carried before it, through the first two or three hundred yards of its course, a part of the breastwork, which, though low, was yet several feet in perpendicular height; but it soon deposited this solid mass, and became a heavy fluid. One house after another it spread round, filled, and crushed into ruins, just giving time to the terrified inhabitants to escape. Scarcely any thing was saved except their lives; nothing of their furniture, few of their cattle. Some people were even surprised in their beds, and had the additional distress of flying naked from the ruins.

William Gilpin stated that well-cultivated land that was rented for twenty shillings an acre prior to the moor surge was not worth sixpence after the inundation. More than twenty-eight families lost their farms and livestock as the flooded moss remained in motion for some four days. Schroeder (1851, vol. 2, p. 182) stated the thick, black water rose 20ft (7m) in height, 'and many of the inhabitants were taken in boats from the roofs of their houses'.

This 'moor surge' was discussed for many years and Clarke (1830) suggested a comparison with a similar event on Chat Moss, a vast peat bog between Liverpool and Manchester, some time between 1509 and 1547: 'The irruption of Solway Moss, in 1771, is well-known, and such an accident occurred to Chat Moss in the reign of Henry VIII, when it disgorged its vast contents into the Mersey, and by its black waters killed the fish.' Further contemporary discussion of the extraordinary Solway Moss irruption of 1771 can be found in the Scottish Geographical Magazine by Withers and McEwen (1989). Meanwhile, across Cumbria and into Northumberland the rains persisted and flooded the rivers Tyne, Wear and Tees, washing away a number of bridges in the torrents that ensued. Late on Saturday 16 November, the Annual Register (1771, p. 155–6) recorded the following account:

. . . the greatest land-flood ever remembered in the memory of man, or any history, came pouring down the river Tine [Tyne], and has done more damage than can be justly estimated; it swelled over all the lower parts of the town; the Sand-hill, which is a large square, where the Exchange and the Courts of Justice stand, was several feet under water, the merchants cellars, warehouses, and shops of eminent tradesmen there, and in a long street, called the Close, contiguous to the banks of the river were six feet under water; the inhabitants were obliged to fly for security to their upper stories. The famous quay here, noted as being the second-best in Britain, for length and breadth, was greatly damaged; several ships lying moored at the cranes were driven from their moorings with only cabbin-boys on board; those whose moorings held firm, were driven upon the quay, and there they must remain till properly launched. The wind and force of the river has greatly shattered the quay, and made a lodgement on it like a wet-dock. The main arch of the seven which our bridge consists of, being a span of seventy five feet [23m], was washed away; the two south arches, with all the houses and shops on the west side, were destroyed and carried down the flood, together with their furniture, stock in trade, account-books, &c. Eight or nine of the shopkeepers, attempting to save some part of their stock, were unfortunately drowned by the fall of the arches and houses; upwards of a hundred coal lighters, that were above the bridge, and treble the number below, were driven down, and many went to sea and sunk.

ETON-MONTEM FESTIVAL

The winter of 1773/4 was a harsh one and January and February 1774 saw deep and penetrating frosts, heavy snow and large tracts of frozen ground. Then came March and the thaws, accompanied by one wet day after another. For twelve consecutive days, the rains came without abating. Mabey (1983, p. 28) quoted an extract from Gilbert White, who wrote on 9 March 1774:

This was the last day of the wet weather: but the waters were so encreased by this day's deluge, that the most astonishing floods ensued. . . . In the night between 8th and 9th a vast fragment of an hanger in the parish of Hawkley [Hampshire] slipped down; and at the same time several fields below were rifted and torn in a wonderful manner . . . 50 acres of ground were disordered and damaged by this strange accident. The turf of some pastures were driven into a sort of waves; in some places the ground sunk into hollows.

By the 12th the Thames was flowing high and ready to burst its banks, taking with it anything in its way. Henley Bridge was destroyed as a result of the swollen river torrents; it was twelve years before a new bridge was opened. There were similar reports of flooding in and around Newbury and Reading, and these indicated both the strength and longevity of the flood waters, which undermined and scoured foundations and led to property being carried away. It was reported that the floods this year were the highest on record at Teddington and the worst flooding of the eighteenth century along the Thames Valley.

Over the centuries, observations of floods have been made by many, including politicians, one of whom was Horace Walpole (1717–97) the son of the first prime minister, Robert Walpole. Horace Walpole was the fourth Earl of Orford, educated at Eton and King's College Cambridge. He toured France and Italy with his friend, the poet Thomas Gray between 1739 and 1741. On his return to England, Walpole became a Member of Parliament and was known as a prolific writer. April and May 1775 had been very warm and dry; Walpole wrote the following account of the weather of early June: 'We have had an extraordinary drought, no grass no leaves no flowers; not a white rose for the festival yesterday! About four, arrived such a flood, that we could not see out of the windows: the whole lawn was a lake, though situated on so high an Ararat.' Here Walpole colourfully refers to his flooded location as an 'Ararat', drawing a comparison between the mountain peak on which Noah's ark landed as the waters of the great flood receded and his location on Strawberry Hill, Twickenham.

It is certainly possible that 'the festival' for which Walpole, as an old Etonian, needed a white rose was the Eton-Montem festival. The Eton-Montem was a time-honoured ceremony peculiar to Eton, said by some to have been coeval with the foundation of the college, and was observed up to the year 1844, when it was abolished. It consisted of a procession of Eton scholars wearing costumes of various periods to a small mount called Salt Hill, for the purpose of collecting money (or salt) for the benefit of the retiring school captain. June was unsettled; there were reported localised thunderstorms, heavy rain and flash floods on the 1st, 10th, 15th and 30th (Gilbert White noted 'prodigious floods' at Hedley, Hampshire on the 15th). The Eton-Montem festival at the beginning of June this year was also subject to a thunderstorm that led to localised flooding. The *Annual Register* (1775, p. 128) noted, 'During the Montem, a yearly festival celebrated on this day by Eton scholars, at Salt-hill there fell the most violent storm of hail and rain ever remembered in that part of the country. The hail-stones were as large as playing marbles, and the sudden flood was such, that several persons were up to the ankles. Most of the many noblemen and gentlemen who were present, were as wet as if they had been drawn through a river.'

HOLMFIRTH, 1777

One of the earliest reported flood events at Holmfirth in West Yorkshire was noted in 1738, after a cloudburst flooded Holmfirth chapel and the surrounding area. It seemed that worse was to come in the last week of July

132

1777 during another similar thunderstorm-induced flash flood, when five bodies were washed out of their graves by the raging torrents. Accounts of the day are varied, but the general consensus seems that the flood waters started at about 8 p.m. and abated at about midnight. The storm and inundation were described by the *Leeds Mercury* (29 July 1777): 'Wednesday evening [23rd], the heaviest storm of rain fell about ten miles above Huddersfield, and on the edge of Lancashire, ever remembered by any person living. It came with such impetuosity off the hills, that it rose four yards in fifteen minutes and a full seven yards higher than usual.' The *British Chronologist* (1789 edn) noted that, 'following a thunderstorm, the water, flowing down from the hillsides, transformed the river into a vast stretch of raging water, by the time it reached Holmfirth it swept all before it, its enormous force crushing down bridges, mills and houses, everything within its reach being gutted or completely wrecked.' The *Leeds Intelligencer* (29 July 1777) described the damage:

> . . . the torrent of water [was preceded by] thunder and lightning . . . many of the houses which stood not near any rivulet were presently under water, and several, with all their furniture, cloaths, utensils, workshops, and stables, together with large quantities of wool, and other goods in trade entirely swept away; some of those houses which resisted the violence of the flood, had their furniture washed out, and hurried away by it; large quantities of corn and grass upon the ground, were utterly spoiled; and no less than seven mills and bridges, were driven down by the rapidity of the current; the water in a little rivulet in the neighbourhood, rose several yards perpendicular in less than ten minutes; three men were carried away by it, to a considerable distance and unfortunately drown'd, one of whom has left a widow and nine children! . . . It is impossible at present to ascertain the damage sustained, but it is supposed to amount at the least to ten-thousand pounds.

The next morning, residents of Holmfirth awoke to find the level ground on the banks of the river covered with mud, stone and wreckage, including broken furniture, machinery and timber.

July 1777 was notoriously unsettled in many places and there were heavy summer rainfalls in Hampshire at the end of the month. A thunderstorm settled over the northern section of the South Downs and affected a triangular area joining Bramshott, Haslemere and Iping. The topography of the area, including that of nearby Blackdown Hill, would have influenced flash flood velocities, which tore large holes in the roads and covered surrounding fields with water and sand. At Haslemere, a post boy was reported to have drowned.

GILBERT WHITE

Gilbert White, curate at the Hampshire village of Selborne, was an English naturalist who made careful observations of his surroundings and recorded these in a systematic way. The prolific writer described one of the first storms of 1781 on 27 February thus: 'Vast Storm. Had the duration of this storm been equal to its strength, nothing could have withstood its fury. As it was, it did prodigious damage. The tiles were blown from the roof of Newton church with such violence, that shivers from them broke the windows of the great farmhouse at rear 30 yards distance' (Mabey, 1983, p. 26). On this occasion the windstorm produced no mention of floods. White (1998 edn) in his text *The Natural History of Selborne* described in a letter to Thomas Pennant, Esq., the reduced water supply to the village after a dry spring and severe hot summer in 1781:

At each end of the village, which runs from south-east to north-west, arises a small rivulet: that at the north-west end frequently fails; but the other is a fine perennial spring, little influenced by drought or wet seasons, called Well-head.* This breaks out of some high grounds joining to Nore Hill [Noar Hill], a noble chalk promontory, remarkable for sending forth two streams into two different seas. The one to the south becomes a branch of the Arun, running to Arundel, and so falling into the British Channel: the other to the north. The Selborne stream makes one branch of the Wey; and meeting the Black-down stream at Hedleigh, and the Alton and

* This spring produced, September 14, 1781, after a severe hot summer, and a preceding dry spring and winter, nine gallons of water in a minute, which is five hundred and forty in an hour, and twelve thousand nine hundred and sixty, or two hundred and sixteen hogsheads, in twenty-four hours, or one natural day. At this time many of the wells failed, and all the ponds in the vales were dry.

Farnham stream at Tilford-bridge, swells into a considerable river, navigable at Godalming; from whence it passes to Guildford, and so into the Thames at Weybridge; and thus at the Nore into the German Ocean.

Interestingly, in a letter dated 25 June 1787 addressed to the Honourable Daines Barrington, White (1998 edn) described in great detail the onset of a violent and sudden flash flood that did considerable damage:

. . . on June 5th, 1784, the thermometer in the morning being at 64 [17.7°C], and at noon at 70 [21.1°C], the barometer at 29, six-tenths one-half [29.65in of mercury, or 1004mb], and the wind north, I observed a blue mist, smelling strongly of sulphur, hanging along our sloping woods, and seeming to indicate that thunder was at hand. I was called in about two in the afternoon, and so missed seeing the gathering of the clouds in the north; which they who were abroad assured me had something uncommon in its appearance. At about a quarter after two the storm began in the parish of Hartley, moving slowly from north to south; and from thence it came over Norton-farm, and so to Grange-farm, both in this parish. It began with vast drops of rain, which were soon succeeded by round hail, and then by convex pieces of ice, which measured three inches in girth. Had it been as extensive as it was violent, and of any continuance (for it was very short), it must have ravaged all the neighbourhood. In the parish of Hartley it did some damage to one farm; but Norton, which lay in the centre of the storm, was greatly injured; as was Grange, which lay next to it. It did but just reach to the middle of the village, where the hail broke my north windows, and all my garden-lights and hand-glasses, and many of my neighbours' windows. The extent of the storm was about two miles in length and one in breadth. We were just sitting down to dinner; but were soon diverted from our repast by the clattering of tiles and the jingling of glass. There fell at the same time prodigious torrents of rain on the farms above-mentioned, which occasioned a flood as violent as it was sudden; doing great damage to the meadows and fallows, by deluging the one and washing away the soil of the other. The hollow lane towards Alton [Hampshire] was so torn and disordered as not to be passable till mended, rocks being removed that weighed 200 weight [about 100kg]. Those that saw the effect which the great hail had on ponds and pools say that the dashing of the water made an extraordinary appearance, the froth and spray standing up in the air three feet above the surface. The rushing and roaring of the hail, as it approached, was truly tremendous.

Writing in Hampshire during October 1786, Gilbert White noted how the first and second weeks of October 1786 brought severe gales and persistent heavy rain to many places, particularly in the south-west, south and south-east of England: 'The newspapers mention vast floods about the country; and much damage has been done by high tides, and tempestuous winds. The hop-planters of this parish from Wey-hill fair with cheerful faces and full purses; having sold large crop of hops for a good price. The hops of Kent were blown away by the storms, after the crop of this county was gathered in' (Mabey, 1983, p. 65).

RIVER FLOODS

Heavy persistent rain and subsequent river floods in Exeter, Devon during October 1786 were noted by Brierley (1964, p. 169): 'The rivers were swollen to an amazing degree and great damage was sustained; the waters rushed through the streets of St Thomas with great rapidity carrying everything before them. At Exwick it made great devastation, and at Stoke about four miles from the City, it threw down 15 houses, besides barns, etc. Several bridges have been thrown down, and we are fearful of hearing still greater mischief done in other parts.'

The *Exeter Flying Post* stated that on the morning of 7 October 1786, flooding from the River Exe in the St Thomas district of Exeter reached a depth of 5ft (1.5m). Interestingly, Brierley (1964) suggested that the floods of October 1786 in Exeter were almost identical to those experienced 174 years later in October 1960.

On 9 February 1791 the River Thames flooded Westminster Hall, and the *Annual Register* (1791, p. 6–7) wrote that the water was considerably higher than it had been in the last twenty years as a result:

New Palace-yard and Westminster-hall were overflowed, and the lawyers were actually conveyed to and from the courts in boats. This has happened several times before, viz. in the years 1235, 1730, February 9, 1735, December 25, 1736, October 14, 1747, and February 9, 1762, but not since. The water rose through the sewers, and overflowed Privy-gardens, great part of Scotland-yard, and some part of St. James's Park. The cellars and kitchens in that neighbourhood were nearly all filled with water. The damage done in the warehouses on the wharfs on both sides the river is immense; they were overflowed almost without exception, as was also the Custom-house quay, Tower-wharf, Bankside, Queenhithe, great part of Tooley-street, Wapping High-street, Thames-street, &c. and all the adjoining cellars filled: most of the gardens and fields between Blackfriars-road and Westminster-bridge were overflowed. The water was so deep in several streets, that boats were used to remove the inhabitants. In New Palace-yard the scuffle for boats was so violent that several gentlemen of the long robe were thrown into the water; and, Westminster-hall not being in the list of regulated fares, the fees insisted on by the watermen were universally complained of as exorbitant. The tides have not increased in height since; for the tide on this night fell short of the great one [which was] three feet nine inches, and that of Thursday [10th] just three feet.

The year 1792 was very unsettled year across the United Kingdom and Ireland, and notable for its wet spring (especially between 6 and 30 April). The floods during April 1792 along the River Liffey, Ireland did considerable damage. A record from Baltinglafs in County Wicklow reported that 'a mill, which has been in bad order, was carried away by the torrent by which accident a boy was killed, and the whole family narrowly escaped ruin.' Just south of Birmingham, at Bromsgrove, Worcestershire, Harman and Showell (1885) reported, 'On April 13, 1792, a waterspout, at the Lickey Hills, turned the Rea into a torrent.' This flash flood event was also discussed in the local Bromsgrove paper *The Gleaner* (July 1855), and recorded in the database by Law *et al.* (2005), who quoted from the *Annual Register* for 1792 as follows:

. . . the inhabitants of Bromsgrove, in Worcestershire, were alarmed and distressed, beyond description, by one of the most sudden and violent inundations known. Between 3 and 4 o'clock, during a storm, accompanied with loud and continued claps of thunder, and the most vivid lightning, a water spout fell upon that part of the Lickey which is nearest the town. The pouring down of the cataract was heard at a great distance, and the body of water, taking a direction towards Bromsgrove, soon swept every thing before it, laid down the hedges, washed quantities of grain from barns and malt-houses, destroyed tanyards, and floated through the town a waggon loaded with skins. The inhabitants had no time to take the necessary precautions; almost in an instant the cellars and under kitchens were filled to the top, and everything in them overturned. In a few minutes the water entered at the parlour windows, covered the counters of the shops, and in the principal street it rose and continued upward of 5 feet perpendicular from the pavement.

The winter of 1794/95 was a very cold one, particularly in the south, with deep penetrating frosts for many weeks, accompanied by heavy snowfalls. The weather journals of the prominent meteorologist Sir Thomas Barker of Lyndon Hall, Rutland, noted in 1795 (Law *et al.*, 2005), 'The frost which began the latter half of December 1794 continued long in this year, an uncommonly severe winter, for a quarter of a year; yet not without a thawing day or two now and then in January.' During the early hours of 26 January 1795 the rain started, and so did the thaw and snow-melt. With the ground still deeply frozen, there was little accommodation for this water to soak away; torrents of water ran down the hills and flooded many areas.

Perhaps the greatest flood involved the River Severn (between 10 and 12 February), where high-volume snow-melt raised the river levels by over 20ft (6m), destroying many bridges in the flood waters' path. Marriott and Gaster (1886, p. 281) drew comparisons with previous flood levels:

The River Severn has overflowed its banks and covered an extent of country for a great number of miles with water. The water continued rising the whole of last Thursday, and its utmost height was only about 7 inches lower than the memorable flood of 1770; but at Bridgenorth it was 6 inches, and at Coalbrookdale 16 inches, higher than at that period. The flood rose in Gloucester to within 6 inches of that in 1770. Shrewsbury was almost surrounded with water. In most places water has risen higher than was ever remembered by the oldest inhabitants; upwards of 50 bridges have been totally destroyed, and a great number of others much damaged.

Elsewhere, Bromwich (2005) provided a report from the *Welwyn Parish Register*, Hertfordshire, which described a:

. . . very hasty thaw and flood: and in the middle of Monday night following; Welwyn town was overflowed by the River [Mimram]; and the houses in the lower rooms were flooded four and some near five feet deep in water. At the bridge, a chimney was drove down, and another damaged so much as it was obliged to be propped from falling, and part of the room and some things in it were carried away down the river to the Mill.

There is no doubt that the eighteenth century provided some very detailed and informed reporting of flooding. The high level of recording has not only aided our knowledge and understanding of flood processes but has provided valuable information in the prevention and management of areas at risk.

Chapter 10

THE NINETEENTH CENTURY

. . . the tidal wave, driven by a hurricane, and bearing on its crest a whole haystack, and debris from the fields below.

(The Revd William Barnes)

By the start of the nineteenth century, the level of reporting was so comprehensive that barely a season went by without a severe flood being recorded somewhere in vast amounts of literature. Floods in the West Country during 1800, especially around the city of Exeter, were detailed by Brierley (1964, p. 169): 'A prodigious flood, such as the oldest person then living had never before witnessed, occurred at Exeter and generally throughout the Kingdom. All the streets in St. Thomas were inundated, the water reaching up to the windows, and these poorer class inhabitants were in great distress.'

There were summer floods in the Herefordshire and Worcestershire area during July 1808, after a period of prolonged heat. The warm period sparked thunderstorms, and Damari (1995, p. 26) noted how on the 15th the skies turned jet black: 'For about an hour and a half in the early afternoon torrential rains fell, with hundreds of houses flooded to a great depth. Thunder continued in what seemed an unbroken roar throughout the storm and the hailstones that fell were like fragments of a vast plate of ice broken into pieces.'

January 1809 was so cold in and around London that heavy rain immediately turned to ice on falling. Eventually the rain melted the snow and ice, but this could not be absorbed by the ground, which was still very frozen;

instead, it went straight into the rivers, which swelled, producing dangerous and damaging floods particularly along the River Thames. During the last week of the month, the height and power of these flood waters was enough to destroy bridges and carry them away. The bridge at Wallingford lost an arch, and so did the Eton-to-Slough Bridge to name but two.

During March 1818, the floods at Oxford were so extensive that *The Times* (1818, p. 3) reported that 'the city looked like a floating island, or like Venice rising from the waters. The navigation of the Thames was entirely stopped, the towing-path being overflowed and invisible.' The nineteenth century brought many Thames floods, and those in November and December 1821 were assessed as some of the worst this century, where water reached halfway up the sides of buildings in the market place at Kingston.

NOVEMBER 1824

One of the most interesting events of the nineteenth century occurred along the south and south-west coasts during November 1824. Varying reports of a 'hurricane', 'tidal wave' and '30 feet of floodwater' were received. It was said that the sea was so mountainous that the world-famous Chesil Beach in Dorset was completely breached in a number of places, but this is still highly debated. So what really happened on 23 November 1824?

Each year a number of hurricanes form in the warm waters of the Atlantic Ocean and remnants of these are known to affect the United Kingdom; but by definition, true hurricanes never reach the UK – or have not done so as yet. However, storm remnants (ex-hurricanes) that resemble intense depressions can produce the characteristics of a hurricane, with strong winds, torrential rains and storm surges. It is thought that prior to 1824 the most notable and severe example of this type of intense Atlantic depression was in 1703, although, again, the derived hurricane status and exact origins of this weather system are inconclusive. The year 1824 produced a typical mix of weather, with storms in March and a hot summer in many places. During the hot weather in Cumbria, the mayor of Kendal ordered all dogs to be kept fastened up because rabies had broken out. Thunderstorms and wet weather then ensued, particularly in the south-east. In Scotland, near Loch Leven, there was a remarkable fall of sprats and herrings from the sky on 7 July.

Autumn in the south was considered relatively fine, but by mid-November things began to deteriorate; appalling floods occurred along the English Channel, and in the Netherlands and Russia.

On 19 November, a low-pressure weather system moved in from the Atlantic towards the Baltic Sea, accompanied by strong westerly winds that created storm surge conditions in the Gulf of Finland. The topography of the gulf funnelled the storm waters into the mouth of the River Neva and the low-lying areas of St Petersburg with tragic consequences. Over 500 people drowned and more than 400 properties were destroyed. This Atlantic weather system influenced conditions in the North Sea, and another storm surge was pushed south towards the Netherlands and the Zuiderzee. The flood waters surged into the Zuiderzee through the narrow Frisian island channels. Large tracts of land were inundated and dykes collapsed as a result. It was suggested that this flood produced water levels greater than those of 1775 and 1776, when the capital city of Overijssel, Zwolle, was flooded.

Three days later, on the 22nd, the wind blew 'like a hurricane' in the English Channel and created what was to become an infamous storm, which ripped across south-west England leaving death and devastation in its wake. Buildings were torn apart, trees uprooted and livestock drowned as rivers rose and overflowed their banks. Sea walls were breached and piers and quays were swept away as waves and tide reached unprecedented heights. Wrecked vessels littered the coasts of Hampshire, Dorset, Devon and Cornwall and many drowned in what was described as 'extreme flooding by staggering tidal waves'.

The Dorset coast suffered the full brunt of the storm. Lyme Regis resident and historian George Roberts wrote a detailed account of its onset. Just three days after the storm's ferocity, on 26 November 1824, his letter to the editor of the *Sherborne and Yeovil Mercury* was published:

On Monday evening the weather looked exceedingly wild, and the wind, which was blowing a hurricane, appeared settled in the south. An officer of the Customs, an experienced seaman, and native of Lyme, was in the watch-house on the Cobb in the middle of the night, and went to assist someone in mooring a boat, and also in securing a fishing boat of his own. He said the tide was 'flowing' at one a.m., Tuesday, though it ought not by the tide-table, to have been 'low water' until an hour after that time! Some duty calling him to the watch-house he remained there a short time, and again went out to assist in mooring a vessel, when he was surprised at the great rise of the tide. He says it came up to high water mark during neap tides at 3 o'clock which was 5 hours before the time of high water! Before four, the sea had risen to a great height, and some persons who were up to look at their boats, as is usual in sea ports when the weather is tempestuous, forewarned individuals at the Cobb houses of the violent tide, which soon after broke over the walls and it was with difficulty, they were taken out, particularly from the easternmost house.

This was the start of what was to be one of the worst storm surges to hit the Dorset coast. At Abbotsbury, the swannery suffered extensive flooding and waters were recorded to a depth of 22ft 8in (7m). A pole marks the alleged flood level today. After the storm, eighteen bodies were found on the beach. Meanwhile, behind Chesil Beach at Fleet village, James Bowering, a young local boy, was standing with some other boys when he saw, early on the morning of the 23rd, rushing up the valley at Butter Street Cove, 'the tidal wave, driven by a hurricane, and bearing on its crest a whole haystack, and debris from the fields below'. The boys ran for their lives inland to Chickerell, and when they returned they found that five houses had been swept away and the church was in ruins. Years later, George Bowering, parish clerk of Fleet, described what his father James, had seen as a young boy (Le Pard, 1999b):

The sea began to break over the beach at 5 am, the water came up as fast as a horse could gallop. James watched as long as he dared, and then, terrified, ran for his life to Chickerell. The nave of the Church was undermined and demolished, also a cottage hard by and another at the end of Butter Street. Two Cottages near the garden of the old Priest's house were also thrown down, two old ladies living in the Priest's house were rescued from a bedroom window. A hayrick was swept away and seven large fishing boats were washed far inland.

As a result of the terrible destruction, the village of Fleet was moved; the properties to the south of the church were not rebuilt, and neither was the church itself. The chancel, the only surviving piece of the old church, was repaired to become a mortuary chapel for the neighbouring graveyard, which remained the burying place for the old village of Fleet. There is a plaque in the chancel which reads: 'In 1824 a great wave washed over the ridge of Chesil Beach and over the Fleet water and passed onwards, the water reaching a depth of about 30 feet at this point.'

The village of Chiswell (often historically referred to as Chisel, Cheswell or Chissel) fared no better, or perhaps even worse. At the time, the Revd George Chamberlaine (Le Pard, 1999a, p. 15), who was rector of the parish of Wyke Regis, Portland, wrote:

In the eve of this day which will ever be memorable for the dreadful catastrophe which caused such devastation over the whole western coast of the Kingdom, the village of Chisel was nearly destroyed, twenty-six of the inhabitants drowned, and upwards of eighty houses damage or washed down by a tremendous surf which broke over the Chisel Bank and bore everything away with irresistible violence before it. At 9 o'clock a most horrid scene presented itself. The sea ran down the streets of Chisel with sufficient depth of water to float a vessel of a hundred tones burden: and the wrecks of the houses, with the furniture of the poor inhabitants was everywhere strewed on the shore. The Ferry House leading to Portland was washed away and the Ferry Man drowned. The communication between the Island and the mainland was nearly destroyed by the ravages of the sea which carried away the sand bank in the eastern side and rendered the passage four times wider than it was before. In short, a scene of greater distress and misery can hardly be conceived, than was occasioned by this storm. And its dreadful effects will never be effaced from the minds of those who witnessed it.

The fatalities as a result of this flood are poignantly recorded on graves and tombs at St George's Church Portland:

Edith Russell aged 12 years
Elizabeth Russell aged 10 years
daughters of John and Edith Russell who lost their lives by an
overwhelming and tempestuous sea in the village of Cheswell
23 Nov 1824

Nipt in the buds by wind and storm
And by the mighty raging sea
Torn from their parents tender arms
Children that were their parents joy

A chilling verse reads:

The wind and sea its fury broke,
The wondrous works of God bespoke:
Man's dwellings levelled with the ground,
When some were killed and some were drowned.

Some debate has continued for many years as to whether the surge or 'tidal wave' actually made its way clean over Chesil Beach. The Revd George Chamberlaine said that 'the Chisel Bank throughout its whole extent was lowered by 20 to 30 feet.' He continued, 'The tremendous surf which broke over the Chisel Bank took everything away with irresistible violence before it.' Further references to the waters breaching the bank were made by the parish clerk of St George's Church, who wrote, 'November 23rd 1824 on a Tuesday morning about 6 or 7 o'clock a very severe wind about SSW the sea came over the beach and washed down about 25 houses to the foundation and about 75 greatly damaged. 22 men women and children killed or drowned 3 ships came ashore the same day and 2 more a few days after.' Sir Frederick Treves suggested a more certain breach in the shingle: 'Only once has the sea made a breach in this curtain of stones. This was on the day in November, 1824, when the waves hammered a gap in the battlements and flooded the swannery at Abbotsbury to a depth of 22 feet 8 inches, as a pole erect in a field testifies to this day.' All were credible writers and local historians. Sir Frederick Treves was indeed famous for many things. Born in Dorchester, Dorset, he continued a keen interest in Dorset's history even when he left the county to become a famous pioneer in abdominal surgery. He wrote a number of authoritative texts, including the very popular and highly regarded *Highways and Byways in Dorset* (1906), which discussed the 1824 floods along the Dorset coast.

Arkell (1956) in his discussion of a 1954 storm on Chesil Beach highlighted some difficulty in locating legitimate accounts to suggest that the beach was actually breached in 1824. Indeed, he had valid concerns, as the pole erected at Abbotsbury to signify the 'flood depth of 22 feet 8 inches' would mean that the water level would have been virtually at the top of the beach even without any superimposed wave height. Arkell (1947) collected material for a Memoir of the British Geological Survey on the Weymouth district, 1935–8, and in doing so came across a number of historic accounts that suggested that on rare occasions parts of the beach had been washed away. The 1898 Geological Survey (Sir A. Strahan) quoted Leland (1710–12) as writing about 'south-eastern winds breaking through the bank', and Camden (1590) as stating that the Chesil Beach, 'when the south wind rises, gives and commonly cleaves asunder'. In 1824, the most remarkable evidence was presented to emphasis the power of this storm, when a 100-ton sloop was carried so high up the beach she was subsequently relaunched in Portland Roads, the more sheltered harbour waters to the rear of the beach. But this does not indicate that the beach was actually breached, as there was another similar instance in 1853 when a vessel was lifted by the sea and left perched on top of the bank. To understand the complexities of this storm, one must look at the structure of Chesil Beach, how severe the described windstorm was, and indeed whether a 'tidal wave' really did occur as described.

The storm of November 1824 was reported and referred to by many writers as a hurricane. 'It blew a most dreadful Hurricane, such as never been known in the memory of man,' wrote the Revd George Chamberlaine. As previously mentioned, this was not a true hurricane, as by definition such hurricanes form and survive in the warmer waters of the Atlantic Ocean, but remnants of these do move north-west towards Europe as weak ex-hurricanes. It is the passage, speed and low atmospheric pressure associated with these intense depressions that influences the sea state and primes storm surge generation. Once generated, storm surges propagate like tidal waves. The combined effect of a storm surge and a high tide is one of the greatest storm-induced risks to coastal environments and can produce water levels and flooding of devastating proportions. A storm surge, therefore, is the product of such atmospheric forcing on the ocean, but the geography of the seabed and coastline also plays an important role. This is a crucial factor at Chesil Beach, which possesses a long south-westerly wave approach from the Atlantic, deep near-shore waters and a steeply shelving beach; therefore any surging mass of water would have piled relatively unhindered into the beach, with great force.

If we look at the breathtaking dimensions of Chesil Beach, we learn more about flood vulnerability associated with this unique shingle barrier. The beach runs from West Bay (in the west) to Portland (in the east), is over 17 miles (27km) long and increases in height towards the east, reaching a maximum of about 45–50ft (14–15m) above mean sea level near Portland, and 22ft (7m) at Abbotsbury (in the west). Its width is around 500ft (152m) at Abbotsbury and 600ft (182m) at Portland, with an overall maximum of around 650ft (200m). Therefore, some sizeable storm surge is needed to penetrate this barrier-beach. Comparisons of crest height and position between an early survey in 1853 and one in 1993 revealed variable trends, but with net crest recession inland of around 25–55ft (8–17m) in eastern parts, accompanied by a lowering of some 2–6ft (0.5–2m) (Carr and Seaward, 1990). Therefore, an important conclusion drawn from contemporary research is that the beach crest is only sensitive to changes during the most severe storms or swell-wave events and that the beach to the east appears to be more sensitive than that to the west (Bray *et al.*, 2004).

There are several historic records of unusual swell-waves that have affected both eastern and western parts of the beach, causing terrible flooding. One such event is known to have overtopped the beach crest on 13 February 1979, when the beach was suddenly overwhelmed by huge waves. If we look more closely at the 1979 event in comparison to 1824, some interesting similarities are seen. The headlines in the *Daily Mirror* on 14 February 1979 were as dramatic as the event: 'Tide of Fear: Families flee as 60ft waves engulf their homes.' If it were true that the waves had been over 60ft (18.3m), they would have been the equivalent of just over four double-decker buses. The details of the newspaper story were even more dramatic: 'The high tide of horror ripped into the Dorset community just as most families were about to get up. . . . wave after wave crashed over the beach pounding cars into rows of crumpled wrecks and swamping homes with 6ft [1.8m] of water.'

Reports of the extreme seas continued: 'The tide-tortured people of Portland trembled in their beds last night – numb with terror at the mountains of water shattering their lives. Only the brave stayed put as a barrage of 60 foot waves

Hurricane Carol arrived shortly after high tide on 31 August 1954, devastating entire coastal communities along the shores of Connecticut, USA. (© *NOAA*)

Moment of impact! A rare capture of a storm surge as it strikes the Florida, USA, panhandle during Hurricane Eloise on 23 September 1975. (© *NOAA*)

Above: Chesil Beach and the Fleet Lagoon near Abbotsbury, Dorset, 2005, where 'tidal waves' destroyed Abbotsbury Swannery in 1824. *Left*: The flood pole and marker at Abbotsbury Swannery, showing the alleged depth of water on 23 November 1824: '22ft. 8 inches (6.9 mtrs)'. *(Both images © Robert K. Doe)*

Water surges through the eastern end of Chesil Beach, flooding the village of Chesil, Dorset, on 13 February 1979. *(Courtesy Stuart Morris Collection)*

Butter Street Cove, Dorset, 2005, showing the location of the old village of Fleet which was destroyed in the storm on 23 November, 1824. (© *Robert K. Doe*)

An artist's impression of Chesil Beach and the Fleet lagoon, Dorset, at the time of the destruction of the old village of Fleet, near Butter Street Cove, during the storm on 23 November 1824. (© *Chris Chatfield*)

On 16 August 2004 the car park at Boscastle, Cornwall, was overwhelmed within minutes by a flash flood, catching unsuspecting motorists by surprise. But worse was to come as cars were picked up and carried out to sea in a torrent of raging water. (© *Arthur Mason*)

The first of a succession of tsunami waves caused by the Sumatra-Andaman earthquake (magnitude 9.0) crashes ashore at Ao Nang Beach, Indonesia, 26 December 2004. (© *David Rydevik*)

Less than four hours after the Sumatra-Andaman earthquake on Sunday 26 December 2004, and shortly after the arrival of the tsunami, the strong receding flood waters pulled anything mobile out to sea at Kalutara Beach, on the south-western coast of Sri Lanka. (*Courtesy © DigitalGlobe*)

Above and below: Comparative images of Banda Aceh, Indonesia, before and after the tsunami on 26 December 2004. (© *DigitalGlobe*)

Flooding in Carlisle, Cumbria, on 8 January 2005. *Above*: A car floats down Warwick Road, St Aidans. *Right*: Flood water 3–5ft (1–1.5m) deep inundates residential properties; outside the water rises to approximately 6ft (1.8m). (© *Amy Carruthers*)

The aftermath of Hurricane Katrina, 2005. This is a view looking north towards Lake Pontchartrain along Pontchartrain Boulevard, New Orleans, Louisiana, on 29 August 2005. A breach in the levee of the 17th Street Canal was responsible for most of the flooding. (© *Petty Officer 2nd Class Kyle Niemi, US Coast Guard*)

roared into their homes. The rest had hastily snatched what they could salvage and headed to safety – many vowed never to return.'

A depression to the south-west of Cornwall gradually built over twenty-four hours, leading up to 13 February. As it moved in and along the English Channel, it deepened not far off the west Dorset coast. The flood started early in the morning. At 6.15 a.m., Margaret Pay, the owner of the Little Ship Inn on Victoria Square said, 'I looked out the window and saw the dustbin being carried into the square on a torrent of seawater. I dashed downstairs in my nightdress. The passage was piled high with pebbles. The public bar was full of stones.' The surge of water had literally picked the beach up with it as it progressed inland. However, prior to the first surge of water the conditions were relatively quiet and there was just a gentle dawn breeze blowing in from the sea. This was the one main difference, as in 1824 there had been severe gale force winds. A senior meteorological officer at the Royal Naval Base, Portland, witnessed this overtopping, followed later by percolation through the bank, which forced him to abandon his attempt to get to work. Observations suggested that the passage of water went up and over a long section of the beach.

Fortunately, the 1979 event resulted in no human fatalities, although the flood wrecked many lives; for the owners of the Victoria Café it was the end of fifty years' hard work, as, within minutes, the waves carried an ice cream freezer, the shop counter and cash register through the plate-glass window and down the street. At the time, the owner said, 'The last time I escaped death was on the 13th February, 1942, when I became a prisoner of the Japanese. But that was nothing compared to the flood on February 13th this year.' In 1979 Victoria Square, Chesil village, was flooded to a depth of around 4ft (1.2m). The surging flood waters left parked cars piled on top of each other and electricity and gas mains in the causeway broken, and masonry swept through breaches in buildings. 'Then, after Army and Navy emergency services had dashed in to evacuate seventy families, council workers fought a massive battle to seal the massive breach in the sea defences. As they did so, the stunned victims wept openly at the sight of family pets lying dead in the sludge and shingle.'

Essentially, a high spring tide combined with a storm surge from a meteorological disturbance far out to sea drove the long-period swell-waves towards Chesil with a great force that not even the beach could suppress. It was the energy of the long-period waves (some 18 seconds) that contributed to the severe overtopping and subsequent lowering of the beach crest. Wave period is the time in seconds it takes for two consecutive wave crests (or troughs) to pass a fixed point. Eighteen seconds is considered a long period in wave arrival along the Dorset coast, especially in comparison with the local average of around 10 seconds. Shingle beaches like Chesil are susceptible to floods from episodic overtopping, and surge breaching, as well as percolation through the pebbles themselves. These factors all contributed to a combined flood risk.

If we look at other regions affected by the 23 November 1824 storm, we are able to piece together a wider picture of events. Storm damage and floods were widespread, affecting the whole of the English Channel towards the Straits of Dover. In Polperro, Cornwall, nineteen boats were destroyed in the storm. Whole families were destitute and the fishermen had to apply for financial assistance. A fund was soon raised to pay for new fishing boats, the harbour walls were rebuilt and eventually an outer pier was built and paid for by local residents. In Porthleven, the harbour was completely destroyed. Meanwhile, the Plymouth breakwater was badly damaged and, further east at Sidmouth, Devon, there was evidence of high-magnitude coastal erosion and flooding where the cliffs crumbled and fell en masse. It was recounted by Sutton (1973, p. 38) in *A Story of Sidmouth*:

At 4 o'clock in the morning of 23rd November, 1824, a storm of such violence occurred that the family of Bolt, occupying one of the cottages on the shore, had to seek shelter in the house above. Very shortly after, the cottages were swept away. As the day dawned, an appalling sight presented itself. The gardens in front of the houses were laid bare and covered with shingle. The fury of the waves broke in the doors and windows of Wallis's Library and other houses, and people were lowered into boats by knotted blankets from upper windows.

The *Taunton Courier* on 1 December 1824 noted:

We regret that Mr. Stone of The York Hotel, having a numerous family to support, has suffered very considerable damage, not only as regards his house

150

but in the loss of wines and liquors. Mrs. Street of the London Inn, a widow with 3 children has also been deprived of considerable property. Mr. Gale, Linen Draper and Mr. Longman, Druggist, in the Market Place were great sufferers. Mr. Edmonson of Bond St. had his shop of goods completely swept away. We are happy to report that everything will be renewed this season.

Further details are noted by George W.E. Russell (1905) in his works on the Revd Sidney Smith. Smith was a colourful character, who, with his famous wit and his dislike of preaching in a cold church, while canon of St Paul's Cathedral in 1831 complained, 'You might as well try to warm the County of Middlesex . . . my sentences are frozen as they come out of my mouth and are thawed in the course of the summer, making strange noises and assertions in various parts of the church.' Russell highlighted one of Sidney Smith's most famous political speeches, which discussed the impacts of the 1824 storm in Devon:

As for the possibility of the House of Lords preventing for long a reform of Parliament, I hold it to be the most absurd notion that ever entered into the human imagination. I do not mean to be disrespectful, but the attempt of the Lords to stop the progress of Reform reminds me very forcibly of the great storm at Sidmouth, and of the conduct of the excellent Mrs. Partington on that occasion. In the winter of 1824, there set in a great flood upon that town the tide rose to an incredible height the waves rushed in upon the houses, and everything was threatened with destruction. In the midst of this sublime and terrible storm, Dame Partington, who lived upon the beach, was seen at the door of her house with mop and pattens, trundling her mop, squeezing out the sea-water, and vigorously pushing away the Atlantic Ocean. The Atlantic was roused. Mrs. Partington's spirit was up; but I need not tell you that the contest was unequal. The Atlantic Ocean beat Mrs. Partington. She was excellent at a slop, or a puddle, but she should not have meddled with a tempest.

Further eastwards and back towards the Dorset coast, flooding was experienced in Poole and Christchurch harbours, where both quays were submerged. At Christchurch, the wind drove the water into Bridge Street and boats were needed in the town. The lower parts of houses were flooded by up to 3ft (1m) (Le Pard, 1999b). However, the flood depths did not seem to have been as high at Poole and Christchurch as they were in and around Chesil Beach. The dramatic descriptions of the storms that described extensive flooding, and loss of property and life must surely have been influenced by a breach at some point along Chesil Beach. Maybe there is insufficient information to suggest that Chesil Beach was breached in the true technical sense of the term in 1824. Perhaps Arkell was right and historical reporting of such an extreme flood event could have been misconstrued. What about the 1824 flood marker at Abbotsbury? It is so specific – 'Depth of water 22ft 8 inches' – and the plaque in the Old Fleet church clearly records '30 ft of water'. There is no doubt that a devastating flood took place, and that as a result the swans at Abbotsbury were obliterated and the old village of Fleet partly destroyed.

One eyewitness to the floods in 1824 suggested that the sea was level with the top of Chesil Beach, although their perspective may have given a false impression. However, it would seem plausible to suggest that Chesil Beach was overtopped by a set of large, powerful waves, if not actually breached, particularly in certain sections adjacent to Butter Street Cove and Abbotsbury Swannery, and at Chesil village. As a result, the beach crest would have been reduced, but there is no specific evidence available to substantiate this with authority. One thing is certain: a combination of a storm surge, high spring tide and exceptional waves driven by a severe windstorm leaves many coastal areas in fear, even to this day.

In Sussex, the sea knew no bounds in November 1824 and overtopped the defences at Seaford and Brighton, flooding large tracts of the towns. The Brighton suspension chain pier was also badly damaged by the high seas and strong winds, ironically on the eve of its first birthday. This was a spectacular structure based on the innovative designs of Captain Samuel Brown but its fate was pretty much sealed less than ten years later (on 15 October 1833), when the pier was partially destroyed by lightning which buckled the chains and shattered the linking platform. It remained resilient throughout the rest of the nineteenth century and survived the throws of many a terrible coastal storm, but the pier finally succumbed to the ravages of the sea in 1896, when it was destroyed beyond recognition.

CLOUDBURSTS

The summer of 1829 produced a number of very interesting events, including a fall of crabs at Redhill and Bourne Place near Canterbury on 19 July. During August, there were terrible floods between Moray and Angus as a result of torrential rains between the 2nd and 4th, along with 'waterspout activity'. Waterspouts are not generally known for their flooding capabilities, but rather their threat to life and structures in their way. However, in this context it could also mean a dense column of rain, a rain core or shaft. Lauder (1830) in his appraisal of the 1829 floods suggested that this was the case: 'The aurora borealis appeared with uncommon brilliance about the beginning of July, and was frequently seen afterwards, being generally accompanied by windy and unsteady weather, the continued drought having been already interrupted during the previous month by sudden falls of rain, partaking of the character of waterspouts.'

Brooks and Glasspoole (1928) provided further details of the tremendous rains on the 4th as the downpour came mainly with a north-east wind, and its force was such that it penetrated all doors and windows facing in that direction. The rivers Nairn, Spey and Findhorn 'rose above their natural boundaries, and spread a devastating deluge over the surrounding country . . . far exceeding . . . any other that ever affected the same locality'.

There are a number of interesting accounts of this summer storm and the Revd James Grant, minister of Nairn, suggested that rain may not have been the only force at play during the evening of Saturday 1 August as he observed 'a dark cloud hovering over the sea in a straight line between Cromarty and Findhorn'. It soon assumed the shape of a huge black column, with its base resting on the surface of the waters, and its top apparently reaching the clouds. It remained for a considerable time, during which he particularly remarked its circumgyrations to be very distinct. It then became lighter and bluer in colour, until it gradually disappeared.

This ascending waterspout was also seen by Dr Smith and others. The 'circumgyrations' do seem to suggest a waterspout in the true sense of the word, associated with the same storm system that produced the high-intensity rainfall that, according to Brooks and Glasspoole (1928, p. 99):

. . . caused the floods of extraordinary intensity, [exhibited] great persistence, and fell over a wide area, and the total volume of water concerned in the floods was enormous. The damage was very great, in spite of the comparative sparseness of the population in the flooded areas. The Findhorn at its greatest height filled the valley, 200 yards [180m] wide, to a level 17 feet [5.2m] above the normal height of the water; the level is marked by a tablet. . . . the melting on snow on the mountains may have added a little, but the preceding months had been generally warm and dry. In fact the state of the ground before the rain must have diminished rather than exaggerated the flooding.

Flooding and further damage were seen in Scotland on 15 and 16 September 1830 as incessant rain fell in just a few hours, but the locals' recovery from this devastating flood proved a testament to their resilience under such trying conditions, especially during harvest time. At Haddington, the drainage system simply could not cope with the volume of water and a number of houses were flooded, with thick, muddy deposits. The River Tyne rose 5ft (1.5m) above the normal level of its course, and at Kelso the rivers Tweed and Teviot rose to such a height that their tributary streams were flooded, some to an unprecedented degree. At Dumfries, a wheelbarrow left empty on the night before the storm had some 2.5in (63.5mm) of rain in it the following morning. The subsequent flash flooding ruined and washed away harvested crops and, in an extraordinary incident, a cart loaded with corn sailed past Kelso; it was thought to have come from a farm at Eckford further to the south. But recovery was remarkable, as noted in the *Kelso Mail*:

We have accounts from all quarters of casualties caused by the deluge, and in many places the damage done to the standing corn has been very serious. Still the operations of harvest are proceeding with vigour, the showers having generally been succeeded by a brisk wind. Even on Thursday [16th], after the torrents of rain which fell in the morning, many farmers were busy leading in the afternoon, and the crops appeared to be in good condition. On Saturday [18th] the weather was delightful!

Summer flooding continued on 17 August 1840 in the Manchester area in what was described as a repeat of the 1799 devastation: 'The River Mersey and Irwell were swelled by the rain to a height which has not been reached by any summer flood since the disastrous inundation in the year 1799, which is still remembered by many Cheshire farmers, and which also occurred on the 17th August.' The rivers were so swollen and strong that a bridge at Walton, near Preston, was washed away, delaying the coach transport en route to Bolton. The *Manchester Guardian* described in detail the drowning of three people engulfed by the flood waters of the swollen River Irwell:

A carter . . . arriving at a point where the road between Bury and Mr Oram's mill crosses (by a ford) the Holcombe Brook, a very short distance from its junction with the River Irwell, he found that the brook was greatly swollen by the rains, and was advised by some person who saw him not to attempt to cross it. He, however, refused to listen to this advice, and not only got into the cart himself but took with him a women and a child, who were desirous of crossing the brook. He then drove his horse into the water, but before he reached the middle, the force of current overpowered the horse, and compelled it to swerve from the proper course; the cart was overturned, and the whole party were precipitated into the Irwell, and they were all three drowned.

During July 1847 a cloudburst on Bodmin Moor flooded rivers and destroyed bridges. A detailed account in *Old Cornish Bridges and Streams* (Henderson and Coates, 1972, p. 108–10) described the cloudburst as a 'waterspout', but the account reminds us of the unpredictable nature of such high-intensity rainfall events which lead to flash flooding:

On 16th July, 1847, a waterspout burst on Davidstow Moor, the watershed where the Camel and Inney (despite their opposite destinies) take their rise. The water collected in the valleys and forced a passage in two directions, down the Inney and the Camel. A wall of water from 12 to 18 feet [3.7–5.5m] above the usual level of the river swept down the Camel Valley carrying everything before it. It was a hot sultry afternoon with a clear sky, and men working in the fields at Gam Bridge could hardly believe their senses when they saw the water approaching them. Gam Bridge stayed the flood for a moment but soon gave way and the infuriated water attacked Wenford Bridge with a regular bombardment of tree trunks and other things plundered from the meadows. A mineral train happened to be in the station at Wenford Bridge, and the driver with great presence of mind drove his engine at full speed down the valley shouting to the people to leave the riverside. He was not a moment too soon. Wenford Bridge broke beneath the strain and Poleys Bridge followed suit. Tresarret Bridge was swept away. Helland Bridge showed that the medieval bridge builders knew their business, for despite the depth and narrowness of the valley, the waters failed to break it, but rising above the parapet, swept on and brought their battery of trees and hayricks against the ancient bridge of Dunmeer. This was soon swept away together with the railway bridge by its side. A train was approaching the bridge at the moment of its destruction but the driver was able to bring it to a standstill.

The second wettest year of the nineteenth century was 1852, which brought with it one of the highest Thames floods on record and, in November, what was to become known as the 'Duke of Wellington's Flood' when the horses pulling the Duke's hearse became distressed in the flooded Bath Road near Maidenhead. The *Illustrated London News* (1852) wrote, 'Amid the rise, and perhaps the fall, of empires, amid fear of change perplexing the nations, amid earthquake and flood, a trembling earth and a weeping sky, Wellington was conveyed from his lonely chamber at Walmer to the more splendid halting-place of Chelsea, and from thence to his grave, in the heart of London. The very elements seemed to sympathise with the feelings of living men at the loss of one so mighty as he had been in his day and generation.' At Putney, the towing path was 6ft (2.7m) under water, and the Great Western line was flooded for 4 miles (6km) between Hanwell and Paddington. The heavy and protracted rains caused much flooding, and at Mereside Soham, Cambridgeshire, many cottagers were 'obliged to leave their houses, hundreds of acres completely under water'. Three weeks of severe flooding across the south-east soon followed, particularly at Epsom, Dartford, Lewisham and Charlton.

The 'Great Sheffield Flood' was a disaster that devastated parts of Sheffield on 11 March 1864. The flood occurred following the collapse of the newly completed Dale Dyke Dam at Low Bradfield on the River Loxley. When the dam burst on the filling of the reservoir, it sent a wall of water flooding down the Loxley Valley, through Loxley and Hillsborough, and then down the River Don through central Sheffield and as far as Rotherham. Around 800 houses were destroyed, with nearly 300 fatalities. Bodies swept away by the flood waters were later found as far afield as Mexborough, past Rotherham. *A Complete History of the Great Flood at Sheffield*, compiled by Samuel Harrison (1864), included a chilling description: '[the flood comes down] with a noise like thunder, and sweeps before it houses, mills, men, cattle, trees, rocks, and whatever impedes its march of destruction and death'. The account was followed by a verse:

> All in a moment, crash on crash,
> From precipice to precipice
> An avalanche's ruins dash
> Down to the nethermost abyss;
> Invisible, the ear alone
> Follows the uproar till it dies;
> Echo on echo, groan for groan
> From deep to deep replies.

The force of the water was 'tremendous' and 'inconceivable', and Harrison wrote, 'The velocity of the flood was awful, and, to use the words of Mr. Rawlinson, the Government inspector, after the dam burst, "Not even a Derby horse could have carried the warning in time to have saved the people down the valley."'

FLOODING IN DORSET

The previous chapters have shown that not one county in the United Kingdom has been unaffected by flooding. Britain has a long history of flooding from extreme rainfall, rivers and the sea. At a regional level, the county of Dorset on the south-central coast has been no stranger to the misery inflicted by coastal deluges in particular. Much detailed research has been completed into marine floods in Dorset, located as it is in the English Channel, with increased vulnerability from the western Atlantic approaches (Doe, 2002).

The first notable flood event in this period occurred during a forty-eight-hour storm which commenced on 20 November 1865 and brought flooding to many locations in the west of the county on the 22nd: 'The sea in the West Bay . . . was throwing volumes of water onto Chesil Beach. In Chiswell people removed furniture, with water being some depth.' Communication with neighbouring Portland by railway ceased on the 22nd owing to the quantity of water, which had undermined the railway and rendered the passage of trains dangerous. Many residents in the area drew comparisons with events in 1824 and some regarded these as worse: 'The gales have been between east and west or from an equatorial quarter, and we don't think there are many living who can remember such a hurricane from the south-west since the gale on November 23rd 1824, which destroyed the village of Fleet.' Similar comparisons with 1824 were drawn after the drowning of three residents in Weymouth in early January 1867. The seas were so high and rough that the esplanade was partially destroyed. One local resident was quoted at the time as saying, 'From an early hour on Saturday morning [5th] the wind blew great guns from the south-west accompanied by one of the roughest and highest tides that have been known since 1824.'

The most notable and somewhat unusual flood event occurred along the south coast of England on 23 April 1868 as a result of what was thought to be a set of possible tsunami waves. Lyme Regis, Bridport and Burton Bradstock in Dorset all reported waves of an unprecedented magnitude occurring suddenly, out of calm weather and calm seas. *The Dorset County Chronicle* described how Burton Bradstock was 'inundated by a rush of water from the sea. . . . the sea was calm.' The waves made a clean break over the beach. Although the weather was also calm at Bridport, flooding from abnormally large waves some 20–30ft (6–9m) was reported, making the coastal road temporarily impassable. At Lyme Regis, the sea rose above the Cobb (the famous harbour wall, which has inspired many artists and writers including Jane Austen), with 20–30ft waves rolling ashore accompanied by a deafening roar. It was believed that the cause of this possible tsunami event was the result of tectonic activity located along the Azores–Gibraltar plate convergence that forms the western part of the lithosphere boundary between the Eurasian and African plates.

There are many areas along the Dorset coast that have experienced flooding, often at exceptional and recurring levels. These areas not only highlight the resilience of the inhabitants but also the vulnerability of specific locations. One area to have suffered periodically was in and around Chesil Beach (as previously mentioned with regard to events in 1824). This structure is liable to percolation of water through the pebbles, and overtopping or breaching of its crest from extreme sea levels. On 21 November 1872 the sea off Chesil Beach was 'indescribably rough', with immense, white-crested waves witnessed more than a mile out to sea before they gathered all their strength and broke with the greatest fury on the beach. The paper of the day, the *Southern Times*, wrote, 'Throughout the night the wind continued as violent as ever, causing the sea to run very high and in the lower part of the village of Chesil the water percolated through the beach and inundated some of the houses. And so continues the village's long association with flooding.'

The Times newspaper headline on Monday 15 November 1875 comprised just three poignant, but sadly familiar, words: 'Gales and floods'. This was referring to events between the 13th and 14th that were instigated by a low-pressure system which moved in from the west on the 10th. As the storm built and high tide approached on the morning of the 13th, parts of Weymouth Quay, Dorset were totally flooded, while in other parts of the town the sea came straight over the quay to flood low-lying streets, the whole area described as being like 'one sheet of water', and people were not able to leave their homes until the flood waters had subsided.

The situation was a lot different further east along the coast at Seaford, Sussex, where the tidal flood was up to people's chins, and evacuation was vital for survival. The residents of Seaford were wondering whether this gale, accompanied by one of the most intense downpours in living memory (reported as lasting some eight hours), was ever going to abate, when suddenly on the morning of the 14th, the wind seemed to increase in ferocity and produced a storm surge that broke over the beach and flowed into the centre of the town, with devastating consequences. The shops and houses were battered with flotsam from shipwrecks; bathing machines and their contents were added to the violent flood waters, causing great property damage and necessitating the evacuation of the town. Thankfully, there were no reported fatalities but the flood waters continued along the channel coast to Hastings, where it was regarded as a storm 'unequalled within the living memory of man or within received traditions'. Mountainous waves surged over Hastings parade, and severe flooding to homes was a consequence that not even the most substantial of barricades could prevent. The words written at the time of the flood in *The Hastings Chronicle* summed up the level of the calamity well: 'It is sickening to enter house after house and see such heartbreaking scenes, especially those inhabited by the poorer people whose life, at the best, is a struggle with poverty. Everything is damaged beyond the hope of future utility. . . . we are confident it is not an exaggeration to say that 256 dwellings is the lowest computation which can be made of those who have suffered.'

A FEARFUL CLOUD

January 1881 was notable for its severe and record-breaking snowfalls, and iced rivers as opposed to flooded ones. However, with all such heavy snowfalls, the onset of the thaw can also be fearful. Brooks and Glasspoole (1928) noted a serious flood on 18 January that resulted from the coincidence of a spring tide with a gale from the north-east in the North Sea (experienced as easterly in the Thames estuary and south-easterly in the Channel) and the break-up of the severe frost. The damage on this occasion was accentuated by the floating ice. When the thaw came in the West Country, the rivers Otter and Exe overflowed, causing considerable damage to surrounding properties near Ottery St Mary, Exeter and Exmouth, Devon, where the strong flood waters washed away large portions of land.

Hot weather affected much of southern and south-eastern Britain in July 1881 and it was not long before thunderstorms and associated heavy downpours and flash flooding were generated, extending north into the Midlands and north-west. *The Annals and Stories of Barrowford* (Blakey, 1929) provided a detailed account of events in Lancashire on 5 and 6 July in what was described as the 'greatest flood ever known' and a 'fearful night', during some six hours of 'pyrotechnics' (thunderstorms): 'It is believed that a cloud burst on Pendle [Hill], and the rushing torrent tore along carrying everything within reach away with it. The river overflowed its banks at the Stannery, and formed another river in Gisburn Road. For the second time we, who lived on the river bank at the shops opposite the Council Offices, found we were on an

160

island, and deemed it safer to get on the mainland. Huge pieces of timber were deposited in the streets, and the Newbridge district was one vast turbulent sheet of water.' Tragically, there was loss of life in the flash floods at Bacup, Lancashire, graphically recounted by Markham (1995, p. 33):

As a little girl was being carried across Burnley Road to safety by her grandfather, a raging current took them both away. The child's lifeless body was found some hours later in Henrietta Street, a half mile distant. In Dawson's Cottages a woman drowned in her cellar abode after a dramatic rescue attempt by her husband. A third victim was swept away after leaving the back door of the Waterloo Hotel. The poor woman's cries for help as she floated down the narrow alley were described as heart-rending by the neighbours.

July 1881 started with floods, and it seemed determined to end with them. The somewhat misleading headline in the *Buxton Advertiser* (6 August 1881) read, 'Tornado in the Goyt Valley', which referred to what was more likely a dark, thick, rain core or rain-shaft that resembled the visual outline of a tornado. However, this was indeed the start of high-intensity rainfall that led to catastrophic flooding on 31 July:

One of the most singular occurrences which has taken place since the memorable flood in 1872, was manifested on Sunday afternoon, and while it lasted created very great concern and fears for the safety of both persons and property. It appears that suddenly, or with very little warning, the high wind in the morning, freshened in the afternoon into a storm, and caused either a cloud or a waterspout to burst with great violence near the Cat and the Fiddle at the head of the Goyt Valley, which was quickly flooded to such an enormous extent that the roar of the rushing water could be heard some distance, as it advanced madly carrying trees and stones before it, and in its descent to Whaley Bridge it carried away three foot-bridges, besides sundry planks crossing the stream. In the valley in which the gun-powder manufacturer of the Fernilee Gunpowder Mills Company are situated, the works were deluged, the valley being like an immense lake, the tramways to the various buildings were torn up and washed away, the roads destroyed, and much loose timber carried away. A cottage near, which had only been repaired lately, and inhabited, was half filled, and surrounded with water, the inhabitants managing to escape and obtain shelter elsewhere. Reaching the valley above the Botany Bleach Works of Messrs. Hall Brothers, at Harwich End, the banks of the Goyt became a vast lake; sand, stones, timber, and even a large foot-bridge being carried off and deposited high and dry on the shore after the water had receded. A large wall had its top portion lifted away some distance. At Messrs. Hall's works the water pipes were broken for a great length, and some of the supports of a wooden trough were bent and twisted almost from their places by the force of the flood. The noise of the stream at Whaley Bridge was very great, and the fury of the torrent which moved down in one vast volume was astonishing. It subsided very quickly, though till about 6 o'clock there was a great stream flowing. The banks below Whaley Bridge were torn down and much damaged. At the village of Combs, near Chapel-en-le-Frith, considerable damage was done to the hay crops as the water rolled down the hillsides like small rivers. The large reservoir which supplies the Peak Forest canal was very low at the time, and so was capable of receiving a large portion of the water. Had this not been the case the damage must have been most serious. The water came with such a sudden rush that it rolled down the river course like one huge wave.

A similar cloudburst that occurred on 21 October 1881 in Devon was described in *British Rainfall* (HMSO, 1862–1974), in which 'A waterspout burst, or at any rate an exceptional fall of water occurred, on the high ground [806ft, or 246m, above sea level] known as Little Haldon, about 3 miles [5km] west of Dawlish, and about the same distance N.W. of Teignmouth, Devonshire. The highest amount of rain measured was 2.06 in [5.23cm], at Lower Reservoir, Teignmouth . . . and about 1.75 in. [4.45cm] was measured at most stations in the neighbourhood.' A detailed report on events was published in the journal, based on material prepared for the *Meteorological Magazine* by Mr G.W. Ormerod, who kept a detailed record of rainfall at Teignmouth:

On the morning of Friday, October 21st, the fall of rain was moderate, until about 8 o'clock a.m., when a labourer, standing on a raised terrace that overlooked the farm-yard, saw it filled with water in the course of a few minutes. The pigs below him were saved with difficulty, and such was the case with a cow and a calf; a cart and horse ready to start were nearly washed away, but were saved by the farmer, who went through water that reached above his waist, and he is 5 feet 8 inches in height. The only loss of life was of four fowls and one duck. Earth, sand, and stones were washed down in considerable quantity, and coloured marks on a cart-shed to the right of the brook show that the flood had risen about 5 feet above the ordinary height of the stream. The mass of water that caused this damage appears to have fallen suddenly on the upper part of the hill, and on the hill-sides to the west of Lidwell Farm. . . . The road to Kingsteignton is, I am informed, greatly damaged, being torn up to the depth of 18 inches, and banks of stone, gravel, and rubbish deposited. Similar damage has taken place on the road descending to Ideford; the rush of water has made a hollow, about 3 feet deep, along the centre of parts of the road from Ideford to Luton and the foot-bridge at that place has been washed away.

HARBOUR FLOOD

When two or more flood sources combine at the same time, they produce a combination flood. If persistent rainfall, high river flows and wave and tidal levels converge on one location during a storm, the consequences can be dramatic. A combination flood occurred in the low-lying area of Christchurch harbour, Dorset, on 27 November 1881. The previous twenty-four hours had seen a rapidly building depression that brought with it high winds and heavy rains, swelling the rivers Stour and Avon, which feed into Christchurch harbour. The harbour is offered a degree of protection from the open sea water of Christchurch Bay by Mudeford Sandbank, a low-lying spit of sand extending from Hengistbury Head (and today home to some of the most expensive beach huts in Europe). In 1881, the shape of the sandspit was somewhat longer because of the availability of sediment supply and the unhindered processes that shaped it. The Stour and Avon soon made their presence known on 27 November in what was described at the time as a 'tremendous outpour of freshwater'. The freshwater channel from the harbour to the sea was constantly changing and heavy deposits of sand and shingle at the northern end of the sandbank contributed to what seemed like the progressive enclosure of the harbour.

The local newspaper of the day, the *Christchurch Times*, announced, 'Christchurch is no longer a "blind harbour" a good channel having been opened just . . . by nature itself. The tremendous outpour of freshwater from the harbour and rivers established a shallow channel where it was 20 years ago.'

As the windstorm and rain intensified, so did the potential for flooding by the sea. At high tide on the morning of the 27th, the seas made a clean breach over the sandbank in several places, with the swell running across the harbour towards the mainland and river mouths in what must have been a terrifying sight to those living in harbour properties. The newspaper reporter at the time wrote, 'almost half the male population of Christchurch were gazing with much interest on the heavy seas sweeping over the bank, about 400 yards of which were entirely submerged.'

The culmination of these events flooded the marshes and meadows of Christchurch harbour and numerous properties along the fringes, but thankfully no loss of life was reported. However, the formation of Mudeford Sandbank was altered so much that the old outlet point for harbour waters was said to never be in the same place again.

A RESTLESS YEAR

Three months notable for their weather diversity were recorded in 1883: February was one of the wettest, September was particularly stormy, and October (through to January 1884) produced the most colourful sunsets. These sunsets were the result of volcanic dust in the atmosphere after Mount Krakatau (in the Sunda Straits between Java and Sumatra) erupted on 27 August. The eruption of Krakatau was devastating. It happened with such force that the explosion partially destroyed the island, leaving a crater nearly 1,000ft (300m) deep in the ocean floor. It comes as no surprise that the blast triggered tsunamis, which struck the coastlines of Java and Sumatra with staggering 130ft (40m) waves. Many villages were totally washed away, including the towns of Teluk Betong, Kalimbang, and Merak. Scarth (1999) published a harrowing account from a Javanese field-hand working in paddy fields located some 5 miles (8km) inland on Java, near the town of Merak:

> . . . all of a sudden there came a great noise. We . . . saw a great black thing, a long way off, coming towards us. It was very high and very strong, and we soon saw that it was water. Trees and houses were washed away. . . . The people began to . . . run for their lives. Not far off was some steep sloping ground. We all ran towards it and tried to climb up out of the way of the water. The wave was too quick for most of them, and many were drowned almost at my side.

The exact death toll will never be known; it was estimated at around 36,000, but for many months after the eruption, the Sunda Straits contained the bodies of those who had not been able to escape the enormous waves.

The floods during 1883 in the United Kingdom were in no way comparable with those along the coasts of Java and Sumatra. Heavy, persistent rainfall will naturally put a strain on rivers and their surrounding floodplains and this was no exception for the River Lambourn and, more notably, the River Kennet near Newbury, Berkshire, between 11 and 13 February, after what was described as an 'incessant deluge'. It was not long before their banks burst and Newbury was well under water. A number of attempts to rescue those stranded by the flood waters were made by local firemen in boats.

Back on the south coast, it had been believed by Dorset villagers that after the flooding in 1881, such a storm would never be relived in their lifetime but, two years later, over 1 and 2 September 1883, a repeat performance occurred in the wake of the remnants of an ex-hurricane (which began its life on 24 August). By the time this weather system arrived on the shores of western and southern Britain, winds in excess of 70mph (60 knots) were causing extensive damage, and yet again Mudeford Sandbank was a raging mass of foam. Seas broke across the sandbank long before high water, removing seven beach huts, and then progressed into the properties on nearby Mudeford Quay and at Christchurch harbour. When the gale and flood waters receded, among many items washed ashore were the carcasses of a cow and two sheep, and several barrels of pickled meat.

A YEAR WITHOUT SUMMER

The year 1888 won fame for being wet, wet and very wet, this being induced by what was a cold and sunless year, 'a year without summer'. The situation was made worse by a series of thunderstorms that produced torrential rainfall. As July came to a close, the inclement weather intensified and by 1 August thunder and lightning continued remorselessly, bringing more rain that could no longer soak away in the already presaturated soils.

Chelmsford, Essex suffered a blast of flash flood waters in the early hours of the 1st. Houses were flooded, the water being waist-deep in some, 8ft (2.4m) in others, causing the residents to take shelter on upper floors. The iron London Road bridge was destroyed by the fast-flowing waters; flood debris, including trees, was thrown against it and this, along with scouring and erosion of the supporting stone buttresses, ensured that it was not long before it fell into the raging torrents. Other rivers became swollen and enhanced by the flood waters, including the River Rom at Romford, which had just over 4.5in (115mm) of rain on the 1st. The river burst its banks, flooding numerous residential properties and businesses, including the Ind Coope Brewery, which lost a reported 30,000 empty casks in the waters. Most of these were later rescued downstream.

The heavy rains and flash flooding also caused landslips in Essex, affecting the railway network. Descriptions of the deluge drew comparisons with 'thunderspouts of water descending from the skies in one sudden drop'. Some 40 per cent of the annual rainfall fell in parts of Essex during July and August. It is not suprising that many felt that summer had been well and truly cancelled this year.

HARD RAINS

Dorset is no stranger to high intensity rainfall, and even holds the United Kingdom record for the highest twenty-four-hour total (11in, or 279mm), recorded at Martinstown, near Dorchester on 18 July 1955. As at many of the other locations discussed, rainfall-induced flash flooding can have tragic consequences for settlements in the path of water channelled by local topography. Lyme Regis received a deluge of flash flood waters from one particularly high-intensity rainfall event in May 1890. A local resident described the incident thus: 'The rain poured down as from a huge waterspout confining itself to a comparatively small area.' The majority of this rainfall appears to have fallen over the catchments and hills of the River Buddle towards the north of the town; as this flowed down towards the sea in what was described as a 'perfect torrent', the flash flood waters washed away walls, roads and gardens, and flooded all the houses in its course. At Uplyme, five cottages were flooded to a depth of 8 or 9ft (2.5m) and in Lyme Regis around twenty-five houses suffered flooding of varying degrees. The rainstorm lasted for about an hour and was accompanied by hail, thunder and lightning. The *Southern Times* reporter at the time of the floods wrote, 'Such a storm has probably never been experienced in the neighbourhood – certainly not within the recollection of the oldest inhabitant.'

High August rainfall on the 10th of that month in 1893, at Preston, Lancashire, produced 2in (53mm) of rain in thirty-five minutes and this event is thought to have generated the highest known five-minute fall of rain in the United Kingdom, at 1.24in (31.7mm). August 1893 was a very warm month, with drought more common than flood. The scarcity of water and the longevity of the drought led to leaves falling off trees, leaving them in a bare and most unusual state. The heat triggered major thunderstorms and with them came hard rains, with one event unusually described at Strathnairn, Scotland: 'the rain fell in lumps, in bucketsful, and almost in solid form,' a resident said on 15 August. *British Rainfall* (HMSO, 1862–1974) described how 'a discharge of water from the clouds which has never before been experienced since the roads were made and the bridges built' sent flood waters sweeping away fertile farm land, properties and part of a stone railway bridge.

A number of notable flood events arose in 1894, of which a violent thunderstorm in south-east England on 24 September created a flash flood of such devastating proportions that the rector of Woodham Walter, near Maldon, Essex, made a public appeal in *The Essex Chronicle*: 'I appeal on behalf of the inhabitants whose homes were wrecked and who lost furniture by the great and sudden flood which swept through our village. Many of the cottages are in ruins, the village postmistress has lost her all, three cottages are hopelessly wrecked.'

Almost eight weeks later, on 12 November, continuous heavy rain started to cause serious floods in London, the south and south-east. A total of 8in (203mm) fell in the Thames Valley in twenty-six days. Botley (1947), in his analysis of Thames flood flows, noted that, despite much filtration into the ground, the daily flow at Teddington rose to over 11,000 million gallons: 'When the river is considered "bank high" it is estimated that the flow is around 4,500 million gallons, and in perspective to other notable floods, for example, December 1946–6,700 million gallons was recorded.' As the rains persisted and the gales intensified, within a week many places were under water, especially in and around Kingston and Chertsey. The tributaries of the Thames also suffered as the Kennet, Loddon, Lambourn and Blackwater burst their banks. The Vale of Kennet, Aldermaston, Lower Burghford and Theale were barely recognisable as the flood waters covered the fields, stranding cattle. In Reading, more than 6,000 men were reported to have been driven from their work by the rapid rise of the Thames and the Kennet, including at the Huntley and Palmer biscuit factory, where the insurgent waters extinguished the furnaces. The *Reading Mercury* described what happened in the village of Coley, where, 'The furious storm turned the Holy Brook into a destructive mass of swirling water in which floated cattle and pigs from Fobney Meadows.' Flooding was extensive near Caversham, where nearly all residential property experienced some degree of flooding and the road between Reading and Caversham was impassable. Meanwhile, the *Maidenhead Advertiser* suggested that the flooding 'attained such proportions that it exceeded even that of the memorable flood of 1852'.

'HO! HO! THE WIND AND RAIN!'

The headline of the *Christchurch Times*, Dorset, on Saturday 17 November 1894 read, 'Storms and Floods. Loss of life and damage to property.' The journalist continued, '"Ho! ho! the wind and rain!" This is an old refrain which has been sorrowfully borne in anew on the dwellers in many parts of the south and the west of England latterly. The gales and floods have done immensity of damage over a wide area, the details of which are quite sensational.' This 'sensational' weather was described as 'a tremendous downpour of rain – the storms coming on suddenly – and there have been some rattling hail showers such as is rarely known in the south of England.' In Maiden Newton, Dorset, between 23 October and 16 November, 13in (326mm) of rain fell, which included four consecutive days with over 1in (25mm). The newspaper of the day was quick to point out that 'every inch means a ton's weight of water to an acre of land – or, by measurement, 22,600 gallons per acre.'

There is no surprise that these continuous heavy rains led to widespread, deep and severe flooding in Dorset, especially at Weymouth, Swanage and Christchurch. In Christchurch, houses that had apparently never before been flooded were inundated by several feet of flood water. Boats were used to transport people from one part of the town to another and a number of cattle were lost as the River Stour rose by nearly 15ft (4.5m). The *Bournemouth Guardian* noted a curious incident relating to a litter of piglets: 'It seems that in consequence to the flood a litter of ten pigs were removed to a place of safety, but the mother thinking the new spot unsuitable for her offspring took them back, with the consequence that everyone of them were drowned, with exception of the mother.' Accompanying the rain were strong gale force winds from the south-west and constant rain for over twenty-two hours: 'The wind blew a hurricane and there was considerable damage to trees and also to roofs of houses.' It was no surprise that the gale, together with the heavy rains and spring tides, caused widespread flooding. Such were the extremities of the flood water that it was described by locals as the most severe in some fourteen or fifteen years.

A combination of high tides and heavy rain led to widespread flooding in Poole harbour and Swanage, Dorset during November 1894 (later, in 1896, it was noted by the local council that the trouble from periodic floods in this area following heavy rainfall arose from the combination of inadequate drainage and the local high tides). In Poole harbour the tides had been very high and, coupled with the heavy rains, caused the low-lying parts of the town to be underwater. At Waterloo Foundry, West Shore, Poole Quay, the fires under the boilers had to be withdrawn because of the flood water in the yard. Meanwhile, in Swanage, 5ft (1.5 m) of water flooded homes and shops: 'All the low-lying lands near Swanage were covered with water, and owing to the tide being high and the space under the new shops not being large enough for the exceptional rush of water, every house was quickly inundated, some to a depth of 4 or 5 feet.' The local newspaper stated that the whole of Lord Eldon's building was 3ft (0.9m) under water and all of the inhabitants were woken at 4 a.m. by the inundation, but they were trapped by this new inland sea and could do nothing but remain in their bedrooms and await help.

Rainfall measured 2.81in (71mm) in twenty-four hours (although this was way below the twenty-four-hour-rainfall record held by Martinstown, near Dorchester, Dorset).

The riverbanks were soon overflowing in north Dorset, where the rivers Stour and Avon at Wimborne rose rapidly. The force of the two rivers meeting caused much of the lower portion of the town to be quickly submerged. The roads were rendered impassable for ordinary traffic, and boats were brought into requisition. Water rushed into homes and shops and it was estimated that '£10–£15 will not cover the damage done on the premises occupied by Mr R. Elcock.' By 1894 standards, £10–15 was a substantial sum, and an equivalent today would be approximately £1,245. This may not seem that much for residential flood damage but it must be remembered that furnishings in those years would not be to the standard they are today. The *Bournemouth Guardian* wrote, 'As a sequel to the heavy and continuous rains of the past fortnight, Blandford was visited with two very high floods this week the River Stour overflowing its banks to a great height and inundating the houses in West Street and East Street and other low-lying parts of the town.' The Crown Hotel was flooded to a depth of 21in (0.5 m). Other houses nearer the river suffered more severely, with 4ft (1.2 m) of water recorded in several properties. It is interesting to note that reports of the flooding stated that many of the residents were 'great sufferers and many of their homes will be damp and chilly the whole of this winter'. As a result, the mayor of Blandford distributed a quantity of coal in the hope this would lessen the hardship of winter caused by the flood.

Further west in south Devon, the destruction of property was accompanied by tragedy. A young boy who lived at Heathfield, near Newton Abbot, was returning from Chudleigh Knighton School when he was carried away by the overflowing River Teign. Tragically, the boy drowned and another who was with him had a narrow escape. Nearby, thirty sheep belonging to a cattle dealer at Kingsteignton, which had been placed on the marshes near Newton Abbot, were carried away by the flood waters. The River Dart created a huge breach in the Mill Leat near Totnes. A 'leat' is a name particularly common in the south-west of England for a man-made watercourse, or a makeshift aqueduct. The force of the flood swept away half an acre of land along with a fishery house, the damage being estimated at the time at £1,000 (the equivalent today would be approximately £83,000). Fortunately, the occupants of the building had left before it was lost to the floods, although the horses and cattle were not so lucky and were later found dead, washed down the stream.

At Bath, the water overflowed the banks of the Avon to such an extent that many roads in the city were inundated. Factories and businesses were flooded, while thousands of people were unable to leave their homes as the lower parts of many buildings were under water. The torrential rains were inevitably going to lead to landslides as the soil saturation levels were soon at a maximum. What was described as a serious landslip occurred on the Swindon and South Wales section of the Great Western Railway near Stroud, where the line ran on an embankment above the Thames and Severn Canal.

HIGH TIDES

Gale-force winds coinciding with high tides produced notable North Sea floods during November 1897. Among the areas affected was the Thames estuary, including the rivers Blackwater and Colne. The amplified seas enabled the tidal surge to break down sea walls in a number of places along the Essex coast, flooding some 50,000 acres of low-lying land. The *Essex Naturalist* reported the following:

> At Harwich . . . the spray was breaking over the sea wall, and in a short time fishermen's boats, that had dragged their anchor, were tossed over the wall into the mud. The tide continued to rise and hundreds of people were on the Bath Side to witness a sight never seen before in Harwich. The whole extent of the sea wall from the continental pier to Dovercourt was one large cataract.

By mid-afternoon, boats were being rowed up the main streets of Harwich: 'The whole of the Bath Side was flooded, in some cases the water reached to the ceilings of the lower rooms and got into the bedrooms. On Tuesday morning [the following day], people were imprisoned in their houses and

171

baker boys could be seen rowing down the street and throwing hot rolls into the first floor windows.' The Essex islands did not fair much better: 'At Horsey Island, of one-thousand acres, scarcely a tenth of the land escaped being submerged. At Penit Island, the tide had complete mastery. Between Frinton and Little Holland, a wide gap was caused through which the sea rushed in an indescribable manner, drowning vast numbers of rats and ground game.' Meanwhile, an increase in beach volume occurred at Clacton, where the higher portion of the beach was raised by around 3ft (0.91m) by the sand deposited when the tide ebbed.

The nineteenth century ended with one of the most notable storm-induced coastal flood events along the Dorset coast, on 13 February 1899, affecting locations in the far west of the county at West Bay, all the way along to the east at Christchurch, encompassing Chesil village, Poole and Weymouth. A high tide, reported in the local press as 'The highest tide for 20 years', coincided with a deep low-pressure storm system. At Weymouth, houses in the vicinity of Hope Square suffered severely from the effects of the amplified tide: 'The high tide in the bay presented a grand spectacle, the waves broke over the esplanade with great violence.' Chesil village once again experienced percolation flooding through the beach; at Christchurch the main streets were impassable and children stranded at school in the town centre had to be lifted into Bridge Street to escape the floods. In Poole harbour, waves broke over the quay wall and the lower parts of the town were soon flooded by some 2 to 3ft (0.9m) of water. The *Bournemouth Guardian* wrote, 'Whilst the gale was at its height the sight presented was terribly grand, and even standing on the quay the waves could be seen to break clean over the Sandbanks at the bottom of the harbour.' Similarly, the *Southern Times* noted:

At West Bay the scene presented was one of unsurpassed grandeur, especially when the tides, which have been abnormally high of late, were at their full height. But while one looked on with an admiring eye at the mighty waves as they rolled in with a thunderous roar and struck with terrific force against the pier heads, dashing the water into the air to 30 or 40 feet [9–12m], feelings of sympathy could not but be entertained for those who were so unfortunate as to have their houses flooded with several feet of water, and this in spite of the special precautions that had been taken. The white-crested waves at high tide swept over the piers of the promenade, and the low-lying parts soon became inundated.

The water washed out the boulders that formed the foundations of the West Pier. The fields along the harbour road were several feet under water and many houses, including the West Bay Hotel and Bridport Arms, were flooded.

It is clear, through this long journey of flooding in and around the United Kingdom, that our ancestors have had much to contend with. On occasion, this has encompassed large-scale loss of life, destruction, starvation and the breakdown of law, order and even common morality in the aftermath of floods. One thing is also very clear: our ancestors have suffered and survived floods of phenomenal proportions. Of course, the standard of living, knowledge of the natural environment, quality of property construction and level of flood defence during these times were limited in comparison with the present day. Also, our perception of flooding should not be distorted while considering this chronological discussion. During these centuries, the weather was diverse and the climate fluctuated, with substantial swings and turns. There were numerous summers of severe heatwaves and droughts, and winters of prolonged cold and frosts. There were also countless instances of extreme rainfall. These rains not only produced localised and deadly flash flooding, but also had a significant impact on society and health, for example the persistent summer rains that led to the potato blight and great famine in Ireland and corn failure in Britain during 1845 and 1846. The accounts of people eating grass, sawdust and refuse to fill their stomachs are all too graphic, but very real. It therefore comes as no surprise that the twentieth (and twenty-first) centuries continued to produce extreme rainfall events and flash flooding of devastating proportions.

Chapter 11

THE TWENTIETH AND TWENTY-FIRST CENTURIES

As the water came down many of the mill buildings seemed to shiver and gave the effect of a man trying to get out from under a tarpaulin sheet.

(Frank Booth, Holmfirth, 1944)

Flash floods are sudden and often unpredictable events resulting from massive rainstorms, a rapid snow-melt in mountain regions, or a failure of natural or man-made water defences. Although they may seem relatively rare in the UK, flash floods do occur, often with devastating consequences. Coming usually after torrential rain, these sudden inundations arise when the ground becomes saturated with water so quickly that it cannot be absorbed, leading to 'run-off'. Run-off is part of the hydrological cycle connecting rainfall and channel flow. It occurs when the infiltration capacity of the soil surface is exceeded, and the subsurface can no longer absorb moisture at the rate at which it is supplied. Rainwater collects in surface depressions and is briefly stored, but when these depressions become filled, the water begins to flow downslope. Run-off can cause localised but very severe flooding – flooding that can lead to large-scale damage and loss of life.

Flash floods hit the headlines on a number of occasions during the summer of 2005. There were the dramatic images of festival-goers swimming from tents at the Glastonbury Festival in Somerset on 24 June, but the most damage was caused a few days earlier when a thunderstorm deposited a month's rain on the North Yorkshire Moors in under three hours on 19 June.

A total of 2.75in (70mm) of rainfall was recorded at Hawnby, north of Helmsley, between 4.15 p.m. and 7 p.m., with 2.7in (60mm) in one hour. This seems an incredible amount, given that around 2.75in (70mm) of rain falls on average in June. As a result, buildings were destroyed and farm livestock killed, and many homes had to be evacuated in and around Helmsley, Hawnby and Thirlby. There is a danger of underestimating the threat posed by flash flooding, as the speed at which storms develop can be very rapid. This was by no means the first time flash flooding had occurred on the Yorkshire Moors with disastrous consequences.

HOLMFIRTH, YORKSHIRE, 1944

'A sea on the moors' was the title given to the tragic disaster that befell the town of Holmfirth, Yorkshire, on 29 May 1944 (shortly before D-Day), which happened to be Whit Monday (now perhaps better known as the Spring Bank Holiday) (Doe and Brown, 2005). The small town of Holmfirth is situated in the southern Pennines, in the steep-sided valley of the River Holme. This was not the first time the town and surrounding area had suffered catastrophic flooding. Earlier events are recorded in 1738, 1777, 1867 and 1931; but by far the worst in terms of human tragedy was on 5 February 1852, when, following several weeks of inclement weather and copious rainfall, the dam holding the Bilberry Reservoir, which was in a poor state of repair, collapsed, and the entire contents of the reservoir rushed down the valley, resulting in eighty-one deaths (Dickinson, 1991). The flood was reported on the front page of the *London Illustrated News* complete with an artist's impression of the devastation, and a public subscription fund soon ensued. Ironically, the disaster led to the first influx of tourists to Holmfirth – via the newly constructed railway line. However, these 'ghouls' were not made welcome in the town.

The thunderstorm that produced the 1944 flash flood came on a very hot day at the end of a predominantly fine May and before the notoriously unsettled June of 1944. In the last week of May a strong anticyclone developed over Spain and the western Mediterranean, while a south-westerly flow of warm air covered the British Isles, associated with a depression near Iceland. That year, 27, 28 and 29 May produced the highest British temperatures on record for those dates, including 91°F (32.8°C) at Horsham,

176

Tunbridge Wells and Regents Park on the 29th (Webb and Meaden, 2000). This was one of those rare occasions when the year's highest temperature was recorded in May.

According to the report produced for the Thunderstorm Census Organisation (Bower, 1944), the storm(s) first developed over central southern England, then travelled north through the Midlands, before climaxing, then dissipating over west Yorkshire. *The Times* on 9 June 1944 printed a report of these storms (wartime secrecy meant that it could not be published earlier). A collection of eyewitness accounts was compiled by J.P. Beveridge (published later in 1982), who carried out a detailed site investigation. A selected chronology of events at Holmfirth for 29 May (*see* Table 4) was published in a detailed account and discussion of events by Doe and Brown (2005), compiled from various accounts of the day and the site investigation notes of Beveridge (1982). The time sequence of events provides a rare and fascinating insight into the onset of flash flooding in and around Holmfirth during the afternoon of 28 May 1944. It also highlights why flash floods are so dangerous and unpredictable:

Table 4. *A selected chronology of events at Holmfirth, 29 May 1944. Times are British Double Summer Time (BDST), 2 hours ahead of GMT. BDST was in operation during the summer of 1944 because of the Second World War daylight-saving initiative.*

Location	Time (BDST)	Notes and Accounts: 29 May 1944
Hillhouse, Cartworth Moor	1425	At 1425 the atmosphere was hot, stuffy and electrical and there were huge black clouds over Holme Moss.
Isle of Skye	1445	Large drops of rain the size of sixpences, then fine by 1445.
Bridge Mills	1600	Thunder started at 1600.
Meltham	1615	Caught in storm about 1615; hailstones the size of mothballs for ten to fifteen minutes.
Blackpool Bridge	1615	Heavy rain.
Overdale	1630	Storm started soon after 1630; the stream rose and covered the cricket field completely in about five minutes; at one time part of Digley Road was under water.

Location	Time (BDST)	Notes and Accounts: 29 May 1944
Bartin, Holmbridge	1630–1700	Blackpool Bridge (which was later destroyed) stream rising between 1630 and 1700.
Holme Valley	1645	Lightning; feeling of being encircled and sulphurous taste in the air.
Digley Valley	1700	Great crack of thunder and torrential rain; lightning persistent.
Holme	1705	Thick mist spreading from Holme and a black vertical cloud wall at the entrance to Digley Valley; like a meteorological cold front – a bank of hot atmosphere meeting another of cold and walling vertically up.
Holmbridge	1705	The progress of the building storm could be seen through Holmbridge and down the valley, but the black bank of cloud remained, blotting out the Digley Valley.
Digley Valley	1725	There was more lightning and a strong gale sprang up; water was rolling down the valley at a great depth.
Cartworth Moor	1725	The channel level was obvious, and flows of water could be seen running out at either side of the bank and meeting in the middle at its foot (no water coming over the embankment itself); thunder and lightning at Cartworth Moor; large drops of rain, increasing in intensity; the horizon from Holme Moss to Isle of Skye was bright orange as if the moors were on fire; as the storm cloud rose higher this belt of colour increased and changed to a nasty blue and then to a dull grey.
Ford Inn – Hinchliffe	1730	A very cold wind and another downpour of hailstones.
While Walls	1730	Spray coming over whole length of Bilberry embankment about 1730; two definite streams running down at each end; the water seemed to be springing up out of the hillside opposite; yard was one foot deep in water.
Holme Village	1730	Heavy rain at 1730 flooding houses at top end of the village; only a shower earlier in the afternoon.
Hinchliffe Mill (north bank)	1730	Heavy rain in Holme (top end of village) started at 1730; came into houses.
2, Bank End	1730–1800	Storm seemed at its worst between 1730 and 1800; water started coming in but stopped when debris was carried down past the back into Digley Road, making a channel for the water.

178

Location	Time (BDST)	Notes and Accounts: 29 May 1944
Holme Bank Bottom	1730–1800	Between 1730 and 1800 cricket ground flooded and water lapping over bridge.
Bray Wood	1740	Start of heavy rain.
Picture Theatre	1745	Rain came down in sheets.
Bartin, Holmbridge	1745–1845	Unable to see embankment between 1745 and 1845.
Deanhouse Mills	1745–1800	The brook was not overflowing at 1745, possibly doing so at about 1800; en route to Hurst House having to wade through 2 feet of water.
Victoria Inn	1750	Mr Lunn left home at 1750 to go to Holmfirth for a paper, doubted whether to take a raincoat.
Bray Wood	1750	Great increase in intensity of rain 'like a monsoon'.
Bray Wood	1755	River a strong winter flow only, but around 1800 rose very quickly (inside a minute) remaining at its height for fifteen to twenty minutes, and then falling again in five minutes – altered its course by Bottoms Mill.
Bridge Mills	1755	Mill dam rose very quickly about 10 feet, then fell gradually; river just covered bridge leading to cricket ground.
Overdale	1755	The main road by the bridge was covered soon after the cricket field and water came up to the café windows 4 feet above road level at about 1755.
Hinchliffe Mill (north bank)	1800	The water rose very quickly (approx 1800) and cleared the bridge; a henhouse was carried away, the water lapped the walls of the lowest houses by the riverside, then came up four steps and soon afterwards began to gradually fall.
Picture Theatre	1800	The river started rising at about 1800 and was soon all but up to the arch, with bales of wool coming down.
Prickleden	1800	Worst around 1800 nearest house to mills.
Bilberry	1800	Storm at its worst, visibility only twenty yards at one time; when it lifted a stream could be seen about six yards wide coming down hillside and falling into Bilberry.
Scar Fold	1800	The water started coming in the bottom houses at 1800 and rose 6 feet altogether; a clock was stopped at 1830; fairly soon after it started to settle.
Upper Bridge	1800–1815	Between 1800 and 1815 saw bales (of wool) coming down, saw Penny Bank go down some time after; bridge to Hollowgate under water all the time.

179

Location	Time (BDST)	Notes and Accounts: 29 May 1944
Flush House	1815	Water eighteen inches deep outside cottages, climbed up through fields to Flush House; lanes a foot deep in water; heavy rain continued to 1900.
Upper Town End, Holmbridge	1815	Unable to see embankment; Hey Clough was a mass of white, several clearly defined streams were rushing down the southern slopes of the valley and it was 'like a sea on the moors' (around Bradshaw); at 1815 Digley Bridge went down.
Holmbridge	1815–1830	River rose 12 feet at Holmbridge, at worst 1815 to 1830; started subsiding about 1840.
William Sykes & Sons	1820	Heard roar of flood water at about 1820; river was constant for about thirty minutes, then rose suddenly about 8 feet at the time the building came down.
Water Street, Hinchliffe Mill (top house)	1820	Grandfather clock in office at Bottoms Mill stopped at 1820, i.e. water up to pendulum 3 feet from floor (rose another 2 feet before falling).
Picture Theatre	1825	People advised to leave the Picture Theatre by the back exit to the main road.
Riverside Mill	1825	Clock stopped at 1825 at Victoria Iron Works.
Upper Bridge	1825	Water rushing through Lower Mill bringing a bale with it; water was 1 foot deep on the bridge opposite the King's Head and half way up the ground floor windows in Hollowgate.
Holme Valley	1825–1900	Height of storm in Holme Valley; as the water came down many of the mill buildings seemed to shiver and gave the effect of a man trying to get out from under a tarpaulin sheet; roaring and crashing could be heard from mills; many buildings seem to be struck by multiple streaks of lightning converging just above them and coming down with a whistle and sharp crack like a whiplash, followed by huge thunderclaps.
Hinchliffe Mill (south bank)	1830	The flood was at its worst at 1830 and above the level of the mill dam 'it looked like one big reservoir'; it was all over in seven or eight minutes and fell to an ordinary 'strong' flow.
Upper Bridge	1830	Caught at Upper Bridge in a deluge which went on until 1830.

Location	Time (BDST)	Notes and Accounts: 29 May 1944
Denham, Newfield	1830	The storm was worst at about 1830; 'there were drops like pennies'; 2 feet of water in the road outside, part of garden scoured away.
Holmeside	1830	Storm was at its worst about 1830.
Deanhouse Mills	1830	At 1830 when the storm was beginning to slacken could see water coming over the embankment in patches.
Hollowgate	1830	The wall on Hollowgate collapsed.
Thongsbridge	1830	Flood started about 1830, began to subside about 1910; electric clock at Albion Mills stopped 1845.
Water Street, Hinchliffe Mill (top house)	1830	The parapet of the bridge went just before 1830.
Holmbridge	1830	Damage done to trees across from river bank.
Newmill Road, Brockholes	1830–1900	Water came into house at Smithy Place Mills and spoiled carpets; flood worst between 1830 to 1900, sharpest rise inside fifteen minutes; rose 9 feet at Smithy Place Mills covering a private bridge
Picture Theatre	1835	At 1825 all people had been evacuated and at 1835 the front entrance (carried on supports over the river) collapsed; looking out of the top window of the Picture Theatre they could see Towngate under water as if there were two separate rivers running at different levels, the second rising to the level of the parapet opposite the Picture Theatre and sweeping up towards the station as far as Milner's foundry.
Hollowgate) (Elephant and Castle	1830–1900	Flood at worst 1830 to 1900 (4 feet 9 inches up building); did not fully subside until 2030.
Hinchliffe Mill (north bank)	1830–2130	The flood came at 1830 exactly and there was still plenty of water at 2130.
Holmbridge	1840	Main road over bridge clear of water at about 1840.
Lower Mytholm-bridge Mill	1845–1900	Flood came between 1845 and 1900 and went down fairly soon; rose about 12 feet (to within a foot of bridge parapet, 8 feet 4 inches deep at bottom of yard).
Towngate	1850	Water rose rapidly.
Mettrick's shop Huddersfield Road	1850	A great swish of water was heard at about 1850 followed immediately by the collapse of a building.

181

Location	Time (BDST)	Notes and Accounts: 29 May 1944
Perseverance Mill	1850–1930	The river was at its height at 1850 and 1930 and the Perseverance Mill dam was covered; the bridge was not flooded but the water was right up to the arch (bottom windows of riverside houses just above not broken); all the damage in the road had been done within twenty minutes of the wall collapsing and three people were carried away.
Water Street, Hinchliffe Mill (top house)	1900	Mill Dam overflowing before 1900; water just came into the garden at worst (came into houses adjoining, occupants out); two footbridges down between Hinchliffe Mill and Bottoms Mill; river rose 12 to 14 feet.
Hollowgate	1900	Flood water 4 feet 6 inches deep in Hollowgate.
Water Street, Hinchliffe Mill (top house)	1900–1915	Yorkshire Penny Bank went down 1900 to 1915 (other buildings 1830).
Prickleden	1900–1930	River at worst 1900 to 1930, up to the grass about 1900 (No. 35) but did not go in house.
Smithy Place	1900–1930	Ankle deep in road at Smithy Place.
Kaye and Messenger Candle works	1910	Water 3 feet deep in front of works at about 1910.
Hope Bank	1915	Flood came about 1915 and lasted about ninety minutes; the footbridge leading to Candle Works was about a foot deep in water and blocked by hen huts.
Rock Mills, Brockholes	1925	Clock stopped at 1925; river rose 9 feet.
Lockwood Bridge	1930	River rose 7 feet just above bridge; did not fall until 2100 to 2130.
Crossley Mills, Honley	1930–1945	A rise of Goit by 4 feet between 1930 and 1945 river rose 10 feet.
Victoria Square	1940	Water sixteen inches deep.
Queen's Square Mill, Honley	1950–2010	River rose 5 feet 6 inches between 1950 and 2010, then fell ten inches to 2030.
Kaye and Stewarts	1955	River started rising rapidly at 1955, at height from 2005 to 2050; total rise about 10 feet (2 feet lower than 1931).
Bilberry	2000	At Bilberry soon after 2000, there was a slight trickle at the south end of the embankment, accentuated by a flow down the hillside at right angles to the reservoirs; much more was coming down the byewash and the embankment was being eroded.

Location	Time (BDST)	Notes and Accounts: 29 May 1944
Holme Valley	2000	Heavy rain lasted until around 2000, thunder stopped earlier.
Water Street	2045	Water came into yard beyond Water Street at about 2045.

What the sequence of events shows is that after a few brief early showers, the cloudburst broke in the late afternoon over the high moors west and south-west of Holmfirth, and then descended into the town; it reached its peak between 5.30 p.m. and 7.30 p.m. before easing off by around 8 p.m. Intense thunder and lightning, hail and strong squalls of wind (possibly tornadic) accompanied the violent rainstorm. 'Three large black twisted columns' were reported 'coming to ground at Digley, Hinchliffe Mill and Hillhouse.' It is likely that these are descriptions of the rain core affected by turbulence on the edge of the updraft (a small-scale current of rising air). The third column was described as 'a solid thunderspout 100 feet [30m] wide and composed of intense drops driven at high velocity by the wind'. The occurrence of a tornadic squall cannot be discounted, but there is little evidence to corroborate this, mainly because of lack of reporting during the war years. Some significant lightning damage to properties was suggested. At the height of the storm, 'roaring and crashing could be heard from mills; many buildings seemed to be struck by multiple streaks of lightning converging just above them and coming down with a whistle and sharp crack like a whiplash, followed by huge thunderclaps.' It is interesting to note that the intense lightning was accompanied by a sulphurous taste in the air.

Although the impacts of the devastating flooding may have diverted attention from any lightning damage to buildings, this would nevertheless have been an important consideration with such an extreme local storm. Hailstones described as 'the size of mothballs' fell at Meltham at 4.15 p.m. It was not long before reports of flooding were received. Water was 'coming down opposite hillsides in a continuous sheet though stronger in some places than others, like the waves of the sea'. The postmaster at Dewsbury described the moors as 'one sheet of water'. Some of this flood water went west down the Longdendale Valley, but the greater part ran east through the Holme

Valley, where the river rose rapidly by 4 to 5ft (1.2–1.5m) in a few minutes to become a torrent 8ft (2.4m) wide and over 15ft (4.5m) deep. As it rushed towards Holmfirth, the riverbank burst, and at one point changed its course to pass through a mill-yard, where it washed away sheds containing £10,000 worth of rabbit skins. It eroded the foundations of an adjacent main road (the A6024), causing masses of stone and earth to fall into the river; and water pipes and a main sewer were also damaged. There was also extensive damage to roads farther up in the hills in the Marsden Clough area.

In Holmfirth itself, where the torrent arrived shortly after 6 p.m., bales of wool were washed out of warehouses, and coping stones dislodged from walls, to be carried up to 4 miles (6km) downstream. Several bridges, two banks, a grocery shop and a milliner's shop, together with mills and workshops, were either wholly or partly demolished by the water. Approximately 200 houses are thought to have been seriously damaged and more than 100 people had to be evacuated from homes and shops, which were flooded to a depth of up to 6ft (1.8m). At Bridge Road, Mr Norman Marsh saw the river rise behind Bottoms Mill and cover the fields in a matter of seconds. This was a result of the water having been temporarily dammed up against the wooden buildings of Riverside Mills, which then collapsed. A powerful stream swept through the yard, and in a few minutes the stone walls on the south-east bank were 'collapsing like a pile of dominoes'. As the flash flood surged through the town, it carried water-borne debris along with it. Bales of cotton from the mills were thrown against houses. During the height of the flood, a Mr Lewis Hirst and a Mrs Schofield were unable to get along a wall to Milner's foundry; they tried to get into the air-raid shelter, but an intervening wall collapsed, forcing them back to their original wall, where they stayed for 7 to 8 minutes until that in turn collapsed when a bale of cotton smashed into it. They were both carried off. At one point, a rescue attempt was performed that was later officially recognised as an act of gallantry. Geoffrey Riley, a 14-year-old boy who had been watching the events with his father, went into the water to rescue the woman, but both of them became overwhelmed by its force. The father then waded in, in an attempt to rescue them, but while the three of them were edging their way to safety along a wall, it suddenly collapsed, and they were swept along in the torrent. Geoffrey eventually managed to pull himself out, but his father and the woman were carried away to their deaths.

For his actions, Geoffrey Riley was awarded the Albert Medal (an award for civilian gallantry that was superseded by the George Cross). A third person in Holmfirth was also reported to have drowned, but the exact circumstances are unclear. The flood was, however, short-lived, the water subsiding almost as quickly as it had risen but leaving a coating of mud over everything it had touched. Lower down the valley, further damage was reported at Huddersfield and Mirfield.

The Holme Valley was not the only region to experience flooding that day. Some of the extreme run-off went down the western side of the watershed, where it passed through Glossop, Derbyshire. There was extensive flooding to houses, one of which collapsed, and a woman drowned when the bridge she was on was carried away, while at Hadfield (close to Glossop) the railway line was submerged. Records from the Thunderstorm Census Organisation noted that the High Peak District floods on the 29th devastated a 3-mile-long area between New Mills and Little Hayfield (south-east of Manchester and south of Glossop). Trees were uprooted and 'all kinds of debris' washed away, and many cottages and a printworks were flooded. Large hailstones, up to 1in (25mm) in diameter, fell in a number of places from Yorkshire and Lancashire as far south as London. In some places 'clear ice' was said to have fallen. On the following day, heavy thunderstorms developed more widely, especially affecting Wales and Somerset, where, at Bason Bridge, window panes and greenhouse glass were smashed by hail. In Leyland, Lancashire, hailstones approximately 1–2in (25–50mm) in diameter were recorded (Met Office, 1944). In an early-afternoon storm at Street, Hindhayes, large hail reduced visibility to around 200yd (180m). At Chirbury, Shropshire, Col C.S. Price-Davis reported that his lawn was completely white with large hailstones.

As the flash flood surged through Holmfirth, a number of assessments were made as to the depth of the flood waters at particular locations. Flooding started at about 5.30 p.m., with water streaming down the surrounding hillside creating two separate streams of flood water. Between 5.30 and 5.45 p.m., flooding of between 1 and 2ft (0.3–0.6m) was experienced, and by 5.55 p.m. this had increased to 4ft (1.2m) in places. By 6.30 p.m., 6ft (1.8m) of flood water was reported, and this soon rose to between 7 and 9ft (2.1–2.7m) at about 7.30 p.m. The maximum reported rise of the River Holme was between 12 and 14ft (3.6–4.2m), but following the storm it was claimed by locals that the river had risen to a height of more than 18ft (5.4m) in some places (Beveridge, 1982). It is interesting to note that the quoted rise of 10ft (3.0m) at the location of Kaye and Stewarts was '2 feet lower than in 1931'. The river was at its height between 8 and 8.50 p.m., and flood waters started to abate soon afterwards (9–9.30 p.m.) following four hours of terrifying conditions. When the waters subsided, the fluvial landscape had changed considerably, some significant scouring having altered the bed and channel configuration.

It seems that this was more than an extreme rainfall event culminating in a devastating flash flood. Lightning and hail damage (and even possibly tornadic squalls) could have occurred on this day, but it is difficult to assess this wartime disaster fully, as news that might be of interest to the enemy was not always reported. What is known is that, tragically, three people in Holmfirth and one in Glossop drowned, parapets of bridges were washed away, mills were badly damaged and, in the centre of Holmfirth, businesses were destroyed. Hundreds of homes were flooded and surrounding fields were covered with stone, clay and other debris for months. As extreme rainfall goes, this event, with a twenty-four-hour total of 4.5in (114.3mm) (although unconfirmed figures of 4.9–5.9in, or 125–150mm, were reported locally), is still some way off the British record of 11in (279mm) recorded some years later at Martinstown, near Dorchester, Dorset (18 July 1955). But what these figures demonstrate is that summer rainfall can produce high daily totals with devastating consequences in specific environments, especially steep-sided valleys. The Holmfirth flood occurred during daylight, which facilitated escape and rescue; however, the severity of the surging 12–18ft (3.6–5.4m) of water still resulted in the loss of life.

LYNMOUTH, DEVON, 1952

The even more tragic Lynmouth flood of 1952 occurred at night, and night-time floods almost certainly make any rescue operation much more difficult, as residents are likely to be less aware of the developing situation. Indeed, in the words of Delderfield (1974), 'The night of Friday, August 15th 1952, will ever be remembered in North Devon, for within a matter of hours one of the most charming and romantic villages in Britain was visited by a major calamity which became world news.' World news was certainly correct, as this flash flood hit the front pages of many national and international newspapers. The *Sunday Express* (17 August 1952) carried a stark picture and dramatic headlines: 'Lynmouth wiped out by floods', '1,000 homeless'. Thirty-four people were in the official fatality listing, with a further person classed as 'unidentified', making the death toll thirty-five. The small booklet *They Took the Lifeboat up the Mountainside – the Lynmouth Flood, 15th August 1952* by Baker (1978) published the list, which even today makes chilling reading. The *Western Morning News* (Monday 18 August 1952) drew wartime comparisons: 'Deaths on a wartime scale, destruction at Barbrook worse than in the heaviest blitz, hundreds of residents and visitors personally ruined and destitute.'

The first two weeks of August 1952 were very wet in the south-west of England. In the run-up to events on the 15th, the soils had become heavily saturated, so that when a thunderstorm associated with a small frontal depression produced torrential rain over Exmoor, filtration capacities were already nearing maximum levels. It is no surprise that the surrounding river channels could not cope with such an overwhelming quantity of water, producing very rapid flow down the East and West Lyn rivers. The rainfall observer at Longstone Barrow, situated near the headwaters of streams draining down into Lynmouth, recorded 9in (229mm) between 11.30 a.m. on 15 August and 9 a.m. on 16 August, of which it was estimated that around 7in (178mm) fell between 5 p.m. and midnight, and 6in (152mm) between 7 p.m. and midnight (Marshall, 1952). Such a fall of rain in a short period will undoubtedly lead to local flooding, especially when enhanced by regional topography. The *Sunday Express* (17 August 1952) reported:

> . . . the floods struck with terrifying suddenness. After torrential rain the East and West Lyn rivers changed their courses, and in minutes buried villages in foaming brown water, giant boulders, and torn trees. The disaster began with 9 hours of rain on Friday night. Gradually the great bogs up on the moor seeped over, then burst into the rivers. The waters plunged over the banks and cascaded in a straight line down to the sea, carrying all before them in a thunderous roar. They hit Lynmouth in darkness,

The impact of the floods was made worse by several extreme surges which it seems were initiated by a series of blockages caused by fallen trees, boulders, animal carcasses and assorted debris. Landslides and bridges created temporary dams that also impeded the river flow from time to time. The breaching of these temporary dams resulted in a sequence of flash flood surges (Keene and Elsom, 1990). The *Western Morning News* on Monday 18 August 1952 wrote:

> Rapidly mounting floods cascaded down the hillsides gathering in an immense wave of water which rushed seawards. Trees, boulders, buildings and a mass of debris pounded up in vast quantities behind bridges in the upper reaches of the rivers. Then one bridge gave way and masses of water and debris hurtled down the narrow valley. Like a 'house of cards' demolished by the trigger action of one card being removed, so did the bridges collapse one after the other, and it was then that the incalculable weight of water descended on Lynmouth.

A fearsome thunderstorm cloudscape was described by many at the time in the lead-up to the storm. There was thunder and lightning and an 'unusual darkening and colour effect to the sky'. Drivers reported that the cloud-base over the hills of Exmoor was so low that it engulfed them in dense fog. A poem published in the Royal Meteorological Society journal *Weather* shortly after the event, in September 1952, provided a poignant reflection on events:

> Clouds that can float in beauty, airy light,
> And fill our changing skies with loveliness,
> When massed in broad-based towers of thrusting height
> Are potent strongholds of destructiveness.
> Their lightnings slay but few. Their fatal power
> Lies in a weight of waters when released;
> By circumstance of time and place and shower
> And narrow stream-filled valleys so increased.
> Our island need not fear catastrophe
> Such as volcanic countries dread, and yet,
> Here from the clouds has dropped calamity
> Upon a Devon cove in green hills set:

> A lovely village, made for holiday,
> Is now a rock-strewn grave, half washed away.
> *(G.M. Hawksley, 1952; reproduced with kind*
> *permission of the Royal Meteorological Society)*

It took time, but gradually Lynton, Lynmouth and the surrounding environments affected by the flash flood recovered, but those whose loved ones perished will forever mourn their loss.

BOSCASTLE, CORNWALL

Almost fifty-two years to the day, the summer flash floods dramatically returned, this time further south, along the Cornish coast at the resort of Boscastle. Thankfully, on this occasion there was no loss of life (some eight people were taken to hospital and approximately 100 needed assistance to safety). Boscastle is located on the north Atlantic coast of Cornwall. The county's most distinguishing feature is its long and thin peninsular character, and it is one of the warmest and wettest regions in the country, although there is significant variation within the area, largely influenced by proximity to the coast and topography. The village of Boscastle lies within a conservation area amid some of the most beautiful countryside in the British Isles; it is one of the few remaining unspoilt harbour villages in Cornwall and is designated an Area of Outstanding Natural Beauty (AONB).

The flash floods on 16 August 2004 were certainly not the first time that flooding had occurred in the area: there were events in 1950, 1958, 1963, 1968 and 1981, to name but a few (HR Wallingford, 2005). August 2004 will certainly go down in history as one of the most severe the village has experienced. August is statistically the second hottest month of the year, just behind July. August 2004 was a warm month, with a Central England Temperature (CET) of 17.7°C (63.9°F), but it also turned out to be the wettest since 1956. A combination of humid subtropical air masses, slow-moving frontal systems and several hurricane remnants (including one from Hurricane Alex) were all reported as possible reasons for the exceptional wet conditions.

On 16 August, heavy, slow-moving thunderstorms initiated downpours at about midday across south-west England. The highest recorded rainfall for the

189

twenty-four-hour period was 7.8in (200.4mm), at Otterham, about 4 miles (6km) east of Boscastle, with rainfall intensity at peak during the first hour of the storm, between 1 p.m. and 2 p.m. By contrast, locations barely 10 miles (16km) south recorded less than 2mm. In fact, much of Cornwall had a dry and fine sunny day; a maximum temperature of 22.6°C (72.7°F) ensured the beaches were well populated.

While intense rainfall is essential to the onset of flash flooding, the drainage and topography of the surrounding area play a role in determining the scale and impact of an event. The proximity of high ground (Bodmin Moor) and morphology of Trevose Head and Pentire Point to the south-west of Boscastle played an important part in the prolonged in-situ downpour that lasted between four and five hours. In environments like Boscastle, steep-sided valleys accentuate flooding by acting as huge funnels for run-off; this channels the water very quickly down to the sea. The high rainfall falling in such a short time could not be absorbed into the ground and instead surged through the village of Boscastle with great force and speed. The flash flood affected over seventy homes and businesses, with over 100 vehicles badly damaged or swept away by the water, some out to sea.

Flash flooding was not restricted to Boscastle. Properties were flooded in the Canworthy Water, Bude and Helebridge areas. Flash floods also caused damage in Stratton, Widemouth Bay, Lansweden, Kilkhampton, Week Ford, Warbstow, Whitstone and Marshgate. There were also major problems particularly in Otterham and Crackington Haven, where a number of bridges and footbridges were washed away, together with large stretches of road. Three miles north of Boscastle, a motorist en route to the town from Cardiff (Doe 2004c, pp. 14–15) recounted:

Three feet of water surrounded our car, and there was no visibility beyond the bonnet. Our hearts were pounding! Fortunately, we were able to drive through and reach some higher ground where we shared apprehensive but supportive smiles and conversation with some thirty other stranded cars whilst the rain eased and the floodwater receded. Little did we know how close we were to true devastation, having been fortuitously turned back near Boscastle by a passing rambler.

In comparison with the Lynmouth flood the nature of the events was fairly similar, although the large loss of life was thankfully not repeated. Another difference was the shorter time-span of the intense rainfall – some four to five hours at Boscastle, whereas the Lynmouth event produced similar rainfall intensity over about seven hours. Furthermore, a highly influential factor at Lynmouth was the landslides and the large volume of debris that blocked tributary systems on Exmoor and aided the catastrophic surges of water. Major landslides were not so significant at Boscastle, although debris blockages are known to have influenced the flow and, in places, passage of the water, especially at bridges. Lastly, the Lynmouth flood occurred at night, whereas the misfortune that befell Boscastle happened in mid-afternoon. Floods at night almost certainly make any rescue operation much more difficult and residents would have been less aware of the developing situation (communications were also more limited in 1952 in comparison with 2004).

Since the Boscastle floods, many issues surrounding summer flash floods have been raised. One is the suggestion that climatic changes in the past three decades could be part of the reason for the series of intense flooding episodes seen across the United Kingdom in recent years (Environment Agency, 2005a), but it is too early to regard this as proved. It is thought that flash floods will become more frequent under a changing climate, and therefore these will have even greater implications if they occur in vulnerable inhabited areas, especially at night. In theory, climate change should reduce summer rainfall. The situation is not that simple, however, because in general terms the number of 'intense' rainfall events during summer months is likely to decrease, but it is the intensity of the rain on the days that it does occur that is projected to increase. So, in theory, a warmer world could mean more-intense rainfall. Warm air can hold more moisture, and more heat means more evaporation from the oceans to generate more storm clouds. But there is no significant evidence as yet to suggest an increase in extreme rainfall events in the UK, although detailed research continues in this field.

At present there are still gaps in our understanding of how the changing climate will affect the areas currently at risk from flash flooding. Although climate change is expected to increase risk over time, there is insufficient quantified and robust information available to be more specific. While we cannot attribute climate change to any single weather event, heavy summer rainfalls are in line with how climate-change scenarios could affect the weather of the United Kingdom, with hotter, drier summers and more intense local thunderstorms.

Chapter 12

PRESENT AND FUTURE PERSPECTIVES

I saw for myself just how serious the flooding was in Carlisle, and I know from this and previous experience how utterly devastating flooding can be for those affected.

(Elliot Morley, MP, 2005)

As I have been writing this text, the daily newswires and press cuttings relating to global floods have continued to arrive without remission. I was surprised at how many reports arrived each day, every day. These were by no means trivial flood events, but were all very newsworthy items, either resulting in loss of life or significant damage to property and infrastructure. I made a concerted effort to read them all, especially ones from distant shores and little-known islands. It was a depressing task, as some of the accounts were blunt and explicit. Honest and factual reporting, no matter how horrific it may seem, is vital in educating, informing and raising public awareness, especially with regard to struggling underdeveloped countries where aid and assistance are in short supply.

Of all the newswires, those that arrived just after Christmas 2004, covering events in south-east Asia, left the longest lasting impression: 'Bodies hanging from telephone wires and trees,' read one; 'Death and destruction,' read another. Only a tsunami could cause such tragedy and devastation. The television coverage was equally shocking and this brought the concept of a tsunami into every household around the world. An earthquake on

193

26 December, known as the Sumatra-Andaman earthquake (magnitude 9.0), triggered a series of giant waves. These waves flooded coastal zones and overwashed islands with violence and contempt. The tsunami killed approximately 200,000 people, making it one of the deadliest disasters in modern history, although the exact death toll will never be known.

The shores of Indonesia, Sri Lanka, southern India, Thailand and the Maldives, along with numerous other countries and small islands, were devastated. Waves of up to 100ft (30m) caused extreme and unanticipated flooding as far away as the east coast of Africa. The furthest recorded death as a result of the tsunamis occurred at Port Elizabeth in South Africa, 5,000 miles (8,000km) away from the earthquake epicentre. The Kenyan newspaper *Daily Nation* (27 December 2004, 'Ruins: We need to be alert') published the following account: 'We may be thousands of kilometres away, but the wave that wrought such death and destruction across Asia was felt on our shores too. The death toll and the damage can only be termed an act of God. . . . The lesson is that no amount of planning and disaster preparation can counter the angry elements.'

The striking photographs and amateur video footage showed that nearly all of the victims were taken completely by surprise by the monstrous waves. There was no tsunami warning system in the Indian Ocean at the time and therefore it would have been difficult to warn such a vast coastal population of the imminent danger. India's *The Hindu* (27 December 2004, 'Death from the sea') angled its coverage towards the lack of warning, which, if it had arrived in time, could have saved thousands of lives:

Cutting a swathe of death and destruction across the coastal areas of half a dozen littoral countries of the Indian Ocean, the titanic tsunami . . . has plunged the whole region into shock and grief. Nature's ferocity in the form of the tsunami is such a rare phenomenon in the South Asian region that unsuspecting people were completely unprepared for it. . . . The death toll is the more poignant for the fact that the tsunami took more than two hours to reach the Indian coast – enough time to clear the most vulnerable areas, the beaches in particular, if only a warning had come.

Tsunami detection is not straightforward. In deep water, tsunamis possess a relatively low wave height and therefore a network of sensors is required to detect any early signs in conjunction with seismic activity. Such a system was not in place in the Indian Ocean, as tsunamis in this region are relatively rare, despite the fact that earthquakes are recorded frequently. Tsunamis are more common in the Pacific Ocean, where they are triggered by the 'Ring of Fire', the world's largest earthquake belt, otherwise known as the 'circum-Pacific seismic belt'. Around 80 per cent of the world's largest earthquakes occur in this zone. International debate in the aftermath of the tsunami indicated that such a warning system should be implemented in the Indian Ocean. After a United Nations conference in January 2005, it was decided that as an initial step towards an international early-warning programme, an Indian Ocean tsunami warning system should be established.

The tsunami that struck on 26 December was not a single wave, but a succession of waves. Witnesses reported that the third wave in the series was the most powerful and occurred about an hour and a half after the first. DigitalGlobe's orbiting satellite captured an aerial image of the devastation around Kalutara in Sri Lanka about an hour after the first wave hit. It showed not only widespread flooding but also the power of the back-surge of water, creating severe water turbulence offshore. The pre- and post-tsunami satellite images were equally shocking. The tsunami completely overwashed Banda Aceh and, according to the Indonesia National Disaster Relief Co-ordinating Board, the number of people who died in the Aceh province totaled over 115,000. Relief agencies reported that one-third of the dead appeared to be children. This was because children were the least able to resist being overcome by the surging waters. The Christian aid organisation World Vision were one of many organisations on the scene soon after the flood. A report in the *American Daily* (18 January 2005, 'Eye Witness Describes Banda Aceh Tsunami Devastation As "Unimaginable"') highlighted the harrowing aftermath:

> The destruction here is unimaginable. Buildings are crushed, flattened and splintered. Cars and buses look as if they've been picked up and tossed. Bodies in bags line the sidewalks in piles of four, five, six or more. Here and there a corpse lies out in the open. And this is two weeks after the quake. It's hideous. You can smell death in the air as you drive down the streets. The one-two punch of both an earthquake and a tsunami has been devastating. It has to be seen to be believed.

The earthquake and tsunami led to an undisputed human disaster and the floods left a long-lasting mark on the coastal ecosystem, with significant damage to coral reefs, mangroves, sea grasses and estuarine mudflats. A great deal of research and environmental assessment still continues to ascertain the full magnitude of the damage. Early indications from the United Nations Environment Programme (UNEP) revealed that the force of the tsunami completely removed flora and fauna and increased sediment load, which killed sediment-sensitive corals and sea grasses by smothering. Chemical changes also took place in the form of saltwater intrusion and enrichment of the water resulting from increased run-off. There was also severe water pollution from raw sewage and the decomposition of flora and fauna, and of unrecovered bodies. Heart-rending reports from south-east Asia arrived for many months after the tsunami and it was difficult to assess any subsequent global flood event with adequate perspective or comparison.

The final words discussing this extreme flood event will go to Sri Lanka's *Daily News* (27 December 2004, 'An unprecedented calamity'), which not only acknowledged the destructiveness of the disaster, but encouraged human resilience in such desperate times:

Never has Sri Lanka faced a natural disaster on the scale that we witnessed yesterday [26 December]. . . . Sri Lankans had never really experienced earthquakes and tsunamis. They used to be phenomena confined to distant countries. We simply saw them on television or read about them in newspapers. . . . Nature has dealt us a severe blow; but we should be united in the face of its ferocity to be brave and resilient in overcoming the consequences of the disaster.

CUMBRIA, 2005

Flooding was back in the headlines between 6 and 8 January as a windstorm with prolonged heavy rain produced episodic flooding in north Wales, Scotland and the north of England. Up to 15 per cent of the average annual rain fell within thirty-six hours on already saturated land; as a result, flooding was inevitable from both the rivers and surface-water routes. This excess rainfall quickly reached the River Eden, in Cumbria. Unable to cope with such a high load, banks were soon overtopped. The weather system that brought the winds and rain also caused a tidal surge around the north-east coast. This surge exceeded 3ft (1m) in some locations, and at Hull it was the fourth-highest tide since 1969 (Environment Agency, 2005b).

The most widespread flooding occurred at Carlisle, in Cumbria, where approximately 6,000 residents from 3,500 homes were flooded, with record water levels 3ft (1m) above the previous highest flooding level in 1822. The flooding in some areas reached 7ft (over 2m) in depth and took four days to subside. The thousands of residents forced from their homes faced up to a year in temporary accommodation. Tragically, on this occasion there were three deaths – two by drowning and one from trauma. Speaking soon after the flooding on 11 January 2005, the Minister of State (Climate Change and Environment), Elliot Morley MP (2005), said in a statement to the House of Commons:

> The Carlisle major incident plan was activated and many residents were evacuated. Some stayed with family and friends; others have been housed in reception centres. There are continuing problems with the electricity supply and telephone connections to many houses. I saw for myself just how serious the flooding was in Carlisle, and I know from this and previous experience how utterly devastating flooding can be for those affected. The thoughts of the Government – and, I am sure, those of the whole House – are with everyone affected, and especially with those who have lost loved ones. . . . What the Government can, and will, do is to ensure that we provide the investment for the Environment Agency and for others involved in flood defence to undertake works where they are most needed. We have always made it clear that nobody can guarantee that there will not be extreme weather events or flooding, but we can continually reduce risk – as we are doing – by investing in defences and warning systems, and by ensuring that there are efficient and effective emergency arrangements to cope with such extreme events. I repeat that commitment to the House.

Most of the residents of Carlisle were able to make their own way to safety. The valiant efforts of the emergency services rescued many, and saved lives. Volunteers with boats helped evacuate the elderly, the young and the infirm.

With telecommunications lines out of action, cries for assistance were plentiful. One resident recounted, 'I'm just shell-shocked, absolutely shell-shocked at the moment. The water was up to my waist. I just wanted to get away and get warm.'

A RECORD-BREAKING YEAR

The Atlantic hurricane season officially begins on 1 June and lasts until the end of November. At the time of writing, the 2005 season still has a few more weeks to run, but what we do know is that it is a record-breaker, as this season had the most named tropical storms since 1933. It started early on 8 June as Tropical Storm Arlene launched the season. Then Hurricanes Dennis and Emily caused billions of dollars worth of damage. But worse was to come as Hurricane Katrina (23 to 30 August 2005) moved into the Gulf of Mexico and caused catastrophic flooding and windstorm damage to Alabama, Mississippi and Louisiana. A storm surge of some 20–30ft (6–9m) affected Mobile Bay in Alabama, and large portions of the coast between the Mississippi cities of Biloxi and Gulfport were left underwater.

At first, New Orleans seemed to have escaped the worst of the winds as Katrina's eye passed to the east of the city, but the levees that separate the city from the surrounding lakes could not withstand the prolonged high winds, heavy rain and storm surge. The US Army Corps of Engineers reported three breaches in the levee system that protected New Orleans, much of which lies under sea level. As a result, 80 per cent of the city was soon underwater. In some places the flood water was 20 to 25ft (7–8m) deep. This spawned one of the largest relocations of residents in American history.

The canals of the city, as well as the Mississippi River banks and the shore of Lake Pontchartrain are lined with earthen levees that usually keep the low-lying city from being flooded. But as high water and wind from Katrina scoured the levees, large sections washed away, including a section reportedly several hundred feet long along the eastern side of the 17th Street Canal, which separated New Orleans' Jefferson Parish (west) from Orleans Parish (east). The US Coast Guard took some dramatic pictures soon after the levees broke that showed the enormity of the flooding that ensued. Coast Guard

198

Hurricane Katrina intensified into a powerful category 5 hurricane over the warm waters of the Gulf of Mexico, with winds exceeding 175mph (152 knots), before weakening as it neared the coast. *(Courtesy NASA and Jeff Schmaltz, MODIS Land Rapid Response Team)*

crews in helicopters plucked to safety people stranded on the roofs of their inundated houses, while state and local rescue crews used boats to reach residents marooned by the floods. Tragically, over 1,000 fatalities have so far been reported as a result of the floods and windstorm, and it is likely that this figure will rise as floods abate and full recovery takes place. One New Orleans resident said, 'All week long, bodies have been recovered from New Orleans' flooded streets, some taken away to be identified, others tied to lamp posts to stop them floating away.'

As with any long-drawn-out urban flooding, there will be serious health concerns, as, apart from lack of water, food, shelter and sanitation facilities, prolonged flooding can lead to an increase in communicable diseases relating to the contamination of food and drinking-water supplies. Analysts anticipate that Katrina will be the costliest hurricane in US history, surpassing Hurricane Andrew in 1992. Early predictions put damages in excess of $100 billion.

A CHANGING CLIMATE

Little reference has been made within this text to the concepts of 'climate change' and 'global warming'. It was never an intention to angle opinion or bias on this interesting, yet often protracted and sometimes controversial debate. The primary aim was to present a history of floods so that the reader could interpret these, draw comparisons, form perspectives and determine his or her own conclusions and opinions. Much has been written and regurgitated and is still being researched on climate change and issues surrounding global warming, and it will be so for many decades to come. There are, however, a few brief issues that do need to be emphasised when contemplating historic flood events. The first is that climate change is certainly not a new phenomenon. The world's climate has always been changing; we can clearly see evidence of this in the short descriptions of weather and climate over centuries discussed within this text. The current concern is that scientists believe elements of human forcing have contributed towards altering or enhancing these 'natural changes'. Many different future outcomes have been proposed and speculated but there will always be a high level of uncertainty. The important point is we must learn to adapt to these changes, just as our ancestors have done over the centuries.

Preventing extreme weather and associated flooding is impossible; managing the risk is not. Accurate and ongoing assessments of areas at risk are vital, as is communicating the nature of the risk, and planning for it. An estimated £214 billion worth of assets are at risk from flooding in England alone, including homes, businesses and prime agricultural land. Around two million homes have been built on the natural floodplain of rivers or the coast, and under climate change scenarios the risk will no doubt increase. Flood prediction is not an exact science and there will always be elements of uncertainty relating to changes in weather patterns and regional vulnerability.

As we reach the end of this selected and concise history of flood events, most notably for the United Kingdom, one question presents itself: what would happen if one of the most extreme events were to happen again today? Extreme floods have occurred in the past and they will occur in the future, almost certainly leading to higher losses. One of the most interesting debates concerns the implications of a repeat of the 1703 windstorm and floods. Research by Risk Management Solutions (2003) had some startling conclusions:

A repeat of the 1703 windstorm today would be catastrophic in its impacts to buildings, casualties, electricity supply and transport, as well as to the consequent economic and insurance impacts. Individual building values have increased by around x 5,000 since 1700, while the population of the southern part of England has grown by a factor of more than 10. However these multipliers cannot simply be employed for factoring the loss, because roofing standards and the quality of the mortar used in chimney stacks have also improved for most buildings, and the roof represents a smaller proportion of the total value of a property than it did in 1703. There are far more trees in and around houses today than in 1700, when among all of Defoe's descriptions of damage there is no mention of a tree falling on a building. However, even then 'so many trees were everywhere blown across the Road, that till the People were called to saw them off and remove them, the ways were not passable'. As in France after windstorms Lothar and

Martin in 1999, millions of customers would be without power after a repeat of the storm, with power-cuts lasting for more than a month in rural areas.

Risk Management Solutions reconstructed the wind-field of the 1703 storm and superimposed it on the current building stock. They established around eighteen million properties in the footprint of damaging winds. The insured losses from a repeat of this storm today would be an estimated £10 billion. For many insurers the loss would significantly exceed their current reinsurance provisions and would ultimately threaten their future viability. It may seem relatively subjective to apply a historical extreme event in a more contemporary context, but a return period, no matter how long or short, should be considered seriously. It would be difficult to estimate a modern-day fatality figure in comparison to 1703, a time when weather warnings and meteorological knowledge were limited; it does, however, give us something to contemplate when considering the future of extreme flood events in a modern society and changing climate.

Right on cue, and as I write the last few words of this text, my attention is drawn to the daily news-wire that arrives in my inbox. The headlines are: Cuba – 'Heavy coastal flooding in northern and southern Havana'; Haiti – 'Flash floods raise deaths to 26'; Australia – 'Storms cause blackouts, flooding'; Hindu Kush – 'Flash floods are a growing threat to mountain regions'; India – 'Floods hit homes, dams almost full'; Vietnam – 'Floods claim 14 lives'; West Bengal – '13 killed in floods'; Florida – 'Flooding forces out residents'. Yet another daily batch of what seem disastrous global flood events. I can only wonder what tomorrow's headlines will bring.

BIBLIOGRAPHY

This bibliography is composed of direct sources and additional texts for reference.

Acreman, M.C. (1989). 'Extreme rainfall in Calderdale, 19 May 1989', *Weather* 44, 438–46

Anderson, J.R.L. (1970). *The Upper Thames*, London, Eyre Methuen Ltd

Annals (1819). J.G. Graham, *Annals of Ireland, ecclesiastical, civil and military, from the 19th of March 1535 to the 12th of July, 1691*, London, G. Sidney

—— (1826 edn). 'Annales Quatuor Magistrorum', in C. O'Conor (ed.), *Rerum Hibernicarum Scriptores Veteres*, Buckingham, J. Seeley

—— (1851). H. Schroeder, *The Annals of Yorkshire from the earliest period to the present time*, 2 vols, Leeds, Crosby

—— (1864a edn). 'Annales de Margan, etc. (AD 1066–1232)', in H.R. Luard (ed.), *Annales Monastici*, 5 vols, Rolls Series, London, vol. 1

—— (1864b edn). 'Annales Monasterii de Theokesberia, 1066–1263', in H.R. Luard (ed.) *Annales Monastici*, 5 vols, Rolls Series, London, vol. 1

—— (1864c edn). 'Monasterium de Burtona super Trent. Annales Monasterii de Burton, 1004–1263', in H.R. Luard (ed.), *Annales Monastici*, 5 vols, Rolls Series, London, vol. 1

—— (1865 edn). 'Annales Monasterii de Waverleia, 1–1291', in H.R. Luard (ed.) *Annales Monastici*, 5 vols, Rolls Series, London, vol. 2

—— (1866a edn). 'Annales Monasterii de Bermundeseia 1042–1432', in H.R. Luard (ed.), *Annales Monastici*, 5 vols, Rolls Series, London, vol. 3

—— (1866b edn). Richardus de Morins, 'Annales Prioratus de Dunstaplia, 1–1297', in H.R. Luard (ed.) *Annales Monastici*, 5 vols, Rolls Series, London, vol. 3

—— (1866c edn). *Annales Ricardi Secundi et Henrici Quarti, regum Angliae*, H.T. Riley (ed.), Rolls Series, London

—— (1869a edn). 'Annales Monasterii de Oseneia. AD 1016–1347', in H.R. Luard (tr. and ed.), *Annales Monastici*, 5 vols, London, Longmans, Green, Reader and Dyer

—— (1869b edn). Worcester Priory, *Annales Prioratus de Wigornia*. AD 1–1377, H.R. Luard (ed.), London, Longman

—— (1870 edn). *Annals of the Church of Winchester from the Year 633 to the Year 1277*, J. Stevenson (tr. and ed.), Rolls Series, London

—— (1871 edn). *The Annals of Loch Cé*, W.M. Hennessy (tr. and ed.), 2 vols, London, Longman

—— (1887 edn). *Annales Cestrienses*, Lancashire and Cheshire Record Society

Annual Register, or a view of the history, politicks, and literature, of the year (1758–). E. Burke (ed.), J. Dodsley, London

Archer, D.R. (1987). 'Improvement in flood estimates using historical flood information on the River Wear at Durham', First National Hydrology Symposium, Hull

Arkell, W.J. (1947). 'The Geology of the Country around Weymouth, Swanage, Corfe and Lulworth', *Memoirs of the Geological Survey of Great Britain: England and Wales*, Department of Scientific and Industrial Research

—— (1956). 'The effects of storms on Chesil Beach in November, 1954', *Proceedings of the Dorset Natural History and Archaeological Society* 76, 141–5

Ashley, W.J. (1887). *Edward III and his wars, 1327–1360*, London, David Nutt

Baker, W.T. (1978). *They Took the Lifeboat up the Mountainside – the Lynmouth Flood, 15th August 1952*, Barnstaple, William Baker

Baliunas, S. and Soon, W. (2003). *Extreme Weather Events: Examining Causes and Responses*, The Washington Roundtable on Science and Public Policy, George C. Marshall Institute, Washington, DC

Barker, T. (1988 edn). *The Weather Journals of a Rutland Squire*, J.A. Kington (ed.), Rutland Record Series, Oakham, Rutland, Rutland Record Society, vol. 2

Barnard, F.P. (1888). *Strongbow's Conquest of Ireland*, London, David Nutt

Barnes, W.M. (1898). 'Fleet Old Church and its Brasses', *Proceedings of the Dorset Natural History and Archaeological Society* 19, 58–64

Bartholomew de Cotton (1859 edn). *Bartholomaei de Cotton, Monachi Norwicensis, Historia Anglicana: AD 449–1298*, pp. lxxviii, 493, H.R. Luard (ed.), Rolls Series, London

BBC (2005). 'Where I Live Kent. Deal: maps, links and facts', www.bbc.co.uk/kent/places/towns/deal/index.shtml, accessed August 2005

Bede (1883 edn). *Interpolations in Bede's Ecclesiastical History and other ancient annals affecting the early history of Scotland and Ireland*, Peebles, J. Watson

—— (1969 edn). *Bede's Ecclesiastical History of the English People*, B. Colgrave and R.A.B. Mynors (eds), Oxford, Clarendon Press

Bennett, J. (1830). *The History of Tewkesbury*, London, Longman

Bettey, J.H. (1970). *The Island and Royal Manor of Portland: some aspects of its history with particular reference to the period 1750–1851*, Bristol, the Court Leet of the Island and Royal Manor of Portland and University of Bristol

Beveridge, J.P. (1982). 'Like Waves of the Sea: Holmfirth Flood 1944', unpublished booklet

Black, A.R. and Law, F.M. (2004). 'Development and utilization of a national web-based chronology of hydrological events', *Hydrological Sciences Journal* 49, 237–46

Blacker, B.H. (ed.) (1881). *Arlingham, Gloucestershire Parish Register*, vol. 1 of 'Gloucestershire Notes and Queries', Arlingham, Gloucestershire

Blakey, J. (1929). *The Annals and Stories of Barrowford*, Nelson, Blakeys

Botley, C.M. (1947). 'Historic Floods', *Weather* 2 (3), 66–8, Royal Meteorological Society

Bower, S.M. (1944). 'Whit-Monday's thunderstorm', unpublished report in the archives of the Thunderstorm Census Organisation, Tornado and Storm Research Organisation, Oxford

Bowker, J. (1998). *The Complete Bible Handbook. An Illustrated Companion*, London, Dorling Kindersley

Brakenridge, G.R., Anderson, E. and Caquard, S. (2004). *2004 Global Register of Major Flood Events*, Hanover, NH, Dartmouth Flood Observatory, www. dartmouth.edu/%7Efloods/Archives/2004sum.htm, accessed August 2005

Bray, M.J., Carter, D.J. and Hooke, J.M. (2004). *Coastal Sediment Transport Study*, report to the Standing Conference on Problems Associated with the Coastline (SCOPAC), 5 vols, Newport, Isle of Wight

Brazell, J.H. (1968). *London Weather*, London, HMSO

Brierley, J. (1964). 'Flooding in the Exe Valley, 1960', paper no. 6753, *Institution of Civil Engineers Proceedings*, 28, June 1964, 151–70

Bristow, J. (2001). *The Local Historian's Glossary of Words and Terms*, 3rd edn, Newbury, Countryside Books

Britton, C.E. (1935). 'The Cold Winter of 1676–1677', *Quarterly Journal of the Royal Meteorological Society* 61, 261

—— (1937). *A Meteorological Chronology to AD 1450*, Geophysical Memoirs No. 70, London, Meteorological Office Air Ministry, HMSO

Bromwich, K. (2005). 'Welwyn Flood in 1795 and also elsewhere', in Reynolds, C. (2001–5) Genealogy in Hertfordshire, v. September, 2005, www.hertfordshire-genealogy.co.uk, accessed August 2005

Brooks, C.E.P. and Glasspoole, J. (1928). *British Floods and Droughts*, London, Ernest Benn Limited

Brown, P. and Jones, S. (2004). 'Storms kill 10,000 fish in Thames', *Guardian*, 5 August 2004

Bryant, E.A. and Haslett, S.K. (2002). 'Was the AD 1607 coastal flooding event in the Severn Estuary and Bristol Channel (UK) due to a tsunami?', *Archaeology in the Severn Estuary* 13, 163–7

Bulman, S. (2001). 'Crosthwaite Parish', v. 22 February 2001, www.steve bulman.f9.co.uk/cumbria/crosthwaite.html, accessed August 2005

Bulmer, T.F. (1901). *History, Topography and Directory of Cumberland*, Penrith, T. Bulmer & Co.

Camden, W. (1590). *Britannia. Siue florentissimorum regnorum, Angliae, Scotiae, Hiberniae, et Insularum adiacentium ex intima antiquitate*, 2nd pt, p. 762, London, Eliots Court Press

Cannon, J. (ed.) (2002). *The Oxford Companion to British History*, revised edn, Oxford, Oxford University Press

Carr, A.P. and Seaward, D.R. (1990). 'Chesil Beach: Changes in Crest Height, 1965–1990', *Proceedings of the Dorset Natural History and Archaeological Society* 112, 109–12

Catholic Encyclopedia (1913 edn). Herbermann, C. *et al.* (eds.), New York, Encyclopedia Press

Centre for Ecology and Hydrology (2004). *Hydrological Summary for the United Kingdom: August 2004*, Wallingford, Oxfordshire

Chambers History Factfinder (2005). M. O'Neill, (ed.), London, Chambers

Chambers, R. (1874). *Domestic Annals of Scotland. From the Reformation to the Revolution*, 3rd edn, vols 1–3, Edinburgh and London, W. & R. Chambers, www.electricscotland.com/history/domestic, accessed August 2005

Chronicles (1533 edn). *The Chronicles of Fabyan*, 2 vols, London, W. Rastell

—— Holinshed, R. (1577). *The firste volume of the chronicles of England, Scotlande, and Irelande*, London, John Harrison

—— (1811 edn). *The New Chronicles of England and France*, London, J. Rivington

—— (1812 edn). *The Chronicle of John Hardyng*, London, Rivington, pp. xxi, 607

—— (1839 edn). *Chronicon de Lanercost: 1201–1346*, J. Stevenson (ed.), Glasgow, Maitland Club

—— (1844 edn). *Croniques de London, depuis l'an 44 Hen. III. jusqu'a l'an 17 Edw. III*, G.J. Aungier (ed.), London, Camden Society

—— (1848–9 edn). *Chronicon Domini Walteri de Hemingburgh*, H.C. Hamilton (ed.), 2 vols, London, English Historical Society

—— (1849 edn). *The Anglo-Saxon Chronicle: Chronicon Petroburgense*, T. Stapleton (ed.), London, Camden Society

—— (1852 edn). *The Chronicle of the Grey Friars of London*, J.G. Nichols (ed.), London, Camden Society

—— (1853 edn). *The Anglo-Saxon Chronicle: The Chronicle of Florence of Worcester*, J. Stevenson (ed.), London, Seeleys

—— (1854 edn). *The Chronicle of Florence of Worcester*, T. Forester (ed.), London, H.G. Bohn

—— (1856a edn). *The Chronicles of John and Richard of Hexham; Chronicle of Holyrood; Chronicle of Melrose; Jordan Fantosme's Chronicle*, in J. Stevenson (tr. and ed.), Documents respecting Canterbury and Winchester, London, Seeleys

—— (1856b edn). *The Chronicle of Melrose*, J. Stevenson (tr. and ed.), Church Historians of England, London, Seeleys

—— (1858 edn). William Stewart, *The Buik of the Croniclis of Scotland; or, a Metrical Version of the History of Hector Boece*, W. B. Turnbull (ed.), 3 vols. Rolls Series, London

—— (1858–68 edn). *Eulogium (historiarum sive temporis): Chronicon ab orbe condito usque ad annum Domini M.CCC.LXVI*, F.S. Haydon (ed.), London

—— (1859 edn). John de Oxenedes, *Chronica Johannis De Oxenedes*, London, Longman

—— (1860 edn). *Caradoc, Brut y Tywysogion; or, the Chronicle of the Princes*, John Williams (ed.), London, Longman

—— (1861 edn). *Anglo-Saxon Chronicle according to the several original authorities*, B. Thorpe (ed. and tr.), 2 vols, Rolls Series, London

—— (1863–8 edn). *Chronica Monasterii de Melsa*, E.A. Bond (ed.), 3 vols, London, Longman

—— (1865). *Willelmi Rishanger, quondam Monachi S. Albani . . . Chronica et Annales, regnantibus Henrico tertio et Edwardo primo*, AD *1259–1307*, H.T. Riley (ed.), Rolls Series, London

—— (1868–71 edn). *Chronica Magistri Rogeri de Houedene*, W. Stubbs (ed.), 4 vols. Rolls Series, London, Longman

—— (1869 edn). T. Wikes, *Chronicon vulgo dictum Chronicon Thomae Wykes*. AD *1066–1289*, H.R. Luard (ed.), London, Longman

——(1870 edn). J. Amundesham, '*Annales Monasterii S. Albani*', *a Johanne Amundesham, Monacho, ut videtur, conscripti*, AD *1421–1440. Quibus præfigitur Chronicon rerum gestarum in Monasterio S. Albani*, AD *1422–1431, a quodam auctore ignoto compilatum*. H.T. Riley (ed.), London, Longman, Green

—— (1871 edn). *Chronica Gentis Scotorum. Historians of Scotland*, J. Fordun (ed.), Edinburgh, Edmonston & Douglas

——(1872–84 edn). M. Paris, *Matthaei Parisiensis, Monachi Sancti Albani, Chronica Majora*, H.R. Luard (ed.), 7 vols, Rolls Series, London

—— (1874 edn). T. Walsingham, *Chronicon Angliae, ab anno Domini 1328 usque ad annum 1388*, E.M. Thompson (ed.), London, Longman

—— (1875 edn). Ralph of Coggeshall, *Radulphi de Coggeshall Chronicon Anglicanum*, J. Stevenson, (ed.), Rolls Series, London

—— (1880 edn). 'Early Chronicles of Shrewsbury, 1372–1603', in W.A. Leighton (ed.), *Transcriptions of the Shropshire Archaeological and Natural History Society 3*, 221–352

—— (1882–3 edn). *Chronicles of the Reigns of Edward I and Edward II*, W. Stubbs (ed.), 2 vols, Rolls Series, London

—— (1889 edn). A. Murimuth, *Adae Murimuth Continuatio Chronicarum*.

Robertus de Avesbury De Gestis mirabilibus Regis Edwardi Tertii, E.M. Thompson (ed.), Rolls Series, London

——(1908 edn). *The Chronicle of the Abbey of Croyland*, H.T. Riley (tr. and ed.), Bohn's Antiquarian Library, London, Bell & Sons

—— (1910 edn). W. Adams, *Adams's Chronicle of Bristol*, with a prefatory note by Francis F. Fox, Bristol, J.W. Arrowsmith

—— (1914 edn). John of Reading, *Chronica Johannis de Reading et Anonymi Cantuariensis, 1346–1367*, J. Tait (ed.), Historical Series, Manchester, Manchester University Press, vol. 20

—— (1964 edn). *Chronica Buriensis, 1212–1301*, A. Gransden (ed.), London, Nelson

Civil Contingencies Secretariat (2005). 'Carlisle Storms and Associated Flooding – Full Multi-Agency Debrief Report', www.ukresilience.info/flooding.htm, accessed August 2005

Clark, C. (1983). *Planet Earth: Flood*, Amsterdam, Time-Life Books

Clarke, S.R. (1830). *The New Lancashire Gazetteer*, London, Henry Teesdale

Clutterbuck, J.C. (1863). 'The Perennial and Flood Waters of the Upper Thames', *Proceedings of the Institution of Civil Engineers 22*

Coates, H. (1916). 'Floods and Droughts of the Tay Valley', *Transcriptions of the Perthshire Society of Natural Science 6*, 103–26

Currie, I., Davison, M. and Ogley, B. (1994). *The Berkshire Weather Book*, Westerham, Kent, Froglets

Damari, P. (1995). *The Herefordshire and Worcestershire Weather Book*, Newbury, Countryside Books

Davison, M., Currie, I. and Ogley, B. (1993). *The Hampshire and Isle of Wight Weather Book*, Westerham, Kent, Froglets

Davy, Charles (1755). 'The Earthquake at Lisbon, 1755', in E.M. Tappan (ed.) *The World's Story: A History of the World in Story, Song and Art*, 14 vols, Boston, Houghton Mifflin, vol. 5: *Italy, France, Spain, and Portugal*, pp. 618–28 (available online from Halsall, P. (1998) *Modern History Sourcebook*, v. November 1998, New York, Fordham University, www.fordham.edu/halsall/mod/1755lisbonquake.html, accessed August 2005)

Defoe, D. (1704). *A wonderful history of all the storms, hurricanes, earthquakes, &c. that have happen'd in England for above 500 years past*, London, A. Baldwin

—— (1779 edn). *A Tour Through the Whole Island of Great Britain*, 9th edn, Dublin, James Williams

—— (2005 edn). *The Storm*, R. Hamblyn (ed.), Penguin Classics, London, Penguin

DEFRA (2005). *The Threat Posed by Tsunami to the UK*, study commissioned by Defra Flood Management, Department for Environment, Food and Rural Affairs, London, HMSO

Delderfield, E.R. (1974). *The Lynmouth Flood Disaster*, Exmouth, ERD Publications

Deltawerken Foundation (2004). 'St. Elizabeth flood 1 (1404)', Stichting Deltawerken Online, Eindhoven, Netherlands, www.deltawerken.org, accessed August 2005

Dickinson, S.F. (1991). *The Holmfirth Flood of 1852*, unpublished booklet, based on material originally published in 1910 by the *Holmfirth Express*

Doe, R.K. (2002). 'Towards a local coastal storm climatology: historical perspectives and future prediction', *Journal of Meteorology*, UK 27 (268), 117–24

—— (2004a). *Extreme Measures. Continuity Insurance and Risk*, London, Perspective Publishing

—— (2004b). *Water, water everywhere. Continuity Insurance and Risk*, London, Perspective Publishing

—— (2004c). 'Extreme precipitation and run-off induced flash flooding at Boscastle, Cornwall, U.K.', *Journal of Meteorology*, UK 29 (293), 319–33

—— and Brown, P.R. (2005). 'A sea on the moors', *Journal of Meteorology*, UK 30 (299), 163–73

Dyde, W. (1798). *The History and Antiquities of Tewkesbury*, 2nd edn, Tewkesbury, Dyde & Son

Emanuel, K.A. (2005). 'Increasing destructiveness of tropical cyclones over the past 30 years', *Nature* 436, 686–8

Emergency Management Australia (2004). EMA Disasters Database, Bathurst Bay, Queensland Cyclone (incl. Storm Surge), v. June 2004, Victoria, Australia, www.ema.gov.au/ema/emadisasters.nsf, accessed August 2005

Encyclopedia Americana (1833). F. Lieber (ed.), 13 vols, Philadelphia, Carey, Lea & Blanchard

Environment Agency (2004). 'The Boscastle and North Cornwall Flood,

16 August 2004', South West Regional and Area Flood Defence Committee Report, 6 October 2004, Wadebridge, Cornwall, North Cornwall District Council

Environment Agency (2005a). *The climate is changing – time to get ready*, Bristol, Environment Agency

—— (2005b). *Managing flood risk. Dealing with flooding: A review of the floods in northern England and North Wales, January 2005*, Bristol, Environment Agency

Evelyn, J. (1996 edn). *The Diary of John Evelyn*, 3 vols, Great British Diarists, reprint of the 1906 edition, London, Routledge/Thoemmes Press

Fagan, B.M. (2000). *The Little Ice Age: How Climate Made History 1300–1850*, Boulder, CO, Basic Books

Fairs, G.L. (1982). 'A tornado at Hay in Herefordshire in the year 1585', *Journal of Meteorology* 7 (70), 187–91

FEMA (2005). '2004 Hurricane season: recovery information', v. 14 September 2005, Washington DC, www.fema.gov, accessed October 2005

Flight, S. (2004). 'Arlingham, Gloucestershire Parish Register Notes', v. 01 Jan 04, www.glosgen.co.uk/arlingham.htm, accessed August 2005

Foggitt, B. and Markham, L. (1993). *The Yorkshire Weather Book*, Newbury, Countryside Books

Foggitt, W. (1978). *William Foggitt's Weather Book*, Newbury, Countryside Publications

Ford, T., Trenberth, K., Easterling, D. and Rose, J. (1998) *Increased Flooding and Climate Change: Consequences for Human Health*, Washington DC, Environmental and Energy Study Institute

Francis, P. (1992). *Volcanoes – A Planetary Prospective*, Oxford, Oxford University Press

Gaschen, S., Hausmann, P., Menzinger, I. and Schadd, W. (1998). *Floods – an Insurable Risk? A Market Survey*, Zurich, Swiss Reinsurance Company

Gervase of Canterbury (1879 edn). *The Historical Works of Gervase of Canterbury*, W. Stubbs (ed.), 2 vols, London, Longman (1879); London, Trübner & Co. (1880)

Gilpin, W. (1786). *Observations, relative chiefly to picturesque beauty, made in the year 1772, on several parts of England particularly the mountains and lakes of Cumberland and Westmorland*, 2 vols, London, R. Blamire

211

Giraldus Cambrensis (1602 edn). 'Topographia Hiberniae', in W. Camden, *Anglica, Hibernica, Normannica, Cambrica, a veteribus scripta, etc.*, Frankfurt, Claudius Marnius

Gregory, D. (1993). *Wales Before 1536 – a Guide*, Llanrwst, Gwasg Carreg Gwalch

Grieve, H. (1959). *The Great Tide: The Story of the 1953 Flood Disaster in Essex*, Chelmsford, Essex County Council

Griffiths, P.P. (1983). *A Chronology of Thames Floods*, 2nd edn, Report No. 73, London, Thames Water

Halcrow Group (2001). 'Preparing for the Impacts of Climate Change. A Strategy for Long Term Planning and Management of the Shoreline in the Context of Climate Change Predictions', report to SCOPAC, Newport, Isle of Wight

Hamilton, N.E.S.A. (1868). *The National Gazetteer: A Topographical Dictionary of the British Islands*, 3 vols, London, Virtue and Co.

Harman, T. and Showell, W. (1885). *Showell's Dictionary of Birmingham*, Birmingham, Cornish Bros (available online from Project Gutenberg, v. 26 December 2004, Salt Lake City, UT, Project Gutenberg Literary Archive Foundation, www.gutenberg.org/files/14472/14472-h/14472-h.htm, accessed August 2005)

Harris, C.S., Hart, M.B., Varley, P.M. and Warren, C.D. (1996). *Engineering Geology of the Channel Tunnel*, London, Thomas Telford

Harrison, S. (1864). *A Complete History of the Great Flood at Sheffield on March 11 and 12, 1864*, London and Sheffield, S. Harrison (available online from M. Armitage, *The Great Flood at Sheffield – 1864*, v. 2001, Sheffield, Armitage, www.shef.ac.uk/misc/personal/cs1ma/flood/book/w-page1.html, accessed August 2005)

Hawksley, G.M. (1952). 'Lynmouth, 15 August 1952', *Weather* 7 (9), 268

Haydn, J. (1904). *Haydn's Dictionary of dates and universal information relating to all ages and nations*, 23rd edn, London, Ward, Lock, and Bowden

Henderson, C. and Coates, H. (1972). *Old Cornish Bridges and Streams*, Truro, Bradford Barton

Henderson, I. (2001). *Planning Policy Guidance 25: Development and flood risk*, London, Department for Transport, HMSO

Higden, R. (1879–86 edn). *Polychronicon Ranulphi Higden monachi Cestrensis*, London, Longman

212

Hill, G. and Hill, K. (2002). *The People's Law Dictionary*, New York, Fine Communications

HMSO (1862–1974). *British Rainfall*, London

Homer (1857 edn). *The Odysseys of Homer*, G. Chapman (tr.), 2 vols, London, J.R. Smith

Horton, B. (1995). *West Country Weather Book*, Bristol, B. Horton

HR Wallingford Ltd (2005). *Flooding in Boscastle and North Cornwall, August 2004*, Phase 2 Studies Report, Report EX5160, Release 1.0, May 2005, Wallingford, Oxford

Hulme, M. and Jenkins, G. (1998). *Climate Change Scenarios for the United Kingdom*, UKCIP Technical Report No. 1, Oxford, UK Climate Impacts Programme

Izacke, R. (1677). *Remarkable Antiquities of the City of Exeter*, London, Rowland Reynolds

Jefferson, J.B. (1821). *The History of Thirsk*, Thirsk, Robert Peat

Jervoise, E. (1931). *The Ancient Bridges of the North of England*, Westminster, Architectural Press

British Chronologist (1789 edn). G. Kearsley (ed.), 3 vols (2nd edn, 1789), London

Keene, P. and Elsom, D. (1990). *Lyn in Flood. Watersmeet to Lynmouth*, Thematic Trails, Oxford, Oxford Polytechnic

Lagassé, P. *et al.* (2000). *Columbia Encyclopaedia*, 6th edn, New York, Columbia University Press

Lamb, H.H. (1977). *Climate: Present, Past and Future*, London, Methuen, vol. 2: *Climatic History and the Future*

—— (1991). *Historic Storms of the North Sea, British Isles and Northwest Europe*, Cambridge, Cambridge University Press

Landsea, C.W., Nicholls, N., Gray, W.M. and Avila, L.A. (1996). 'Downward trends in the frequency of intense Atlantic hurricanes during the past five decades', *Geophysical Research Letters* 23, 1697–1700

Latham, B. (1904). *Croydon Bourne Flows*, supplement to the Proceedings of the Croydon Natural History and Scientific Society, London, J.B. Nichols and Sons

Lauder, T.D. (1830). *An account of the great floods of August 1829, in the province of Moray, and adjoining districts*, 2nd edn, Edinburgh, Adam Black

213

Laughton, L.G.C. and Heddon, V. (1927). *Great Storms . . . Illustrated*, London, P. Allan, London

Law, F.M., Black, A.R., Scarrott, R.M., Miller, J.B. and Bayliss, A.C. (2005). 'Chronology of British Hydrological Events', Dundee, University of Dundee, www.dundee.ac.uk/geography/cbhe/, accessed August 2005

Leland, J. (1710–12). *The Itinerary of John Leland the Antiquary*, 9 vols, Oxford, T. Hearne

Le Pard, G. (1999a). 'An Awful Visitation. The Great Storm of 1824 and its Aftermath', unpublished booklet, p. 38

—— (1999b). 'The Great Storm of 1824', *Proceedings of the Dorset Natural History and Archaeological Society* 121, 23–36

Lowe, E.J. (1870). *Natural Phenomena: and Chronology of the Seasons*, London, Bell and Daldy

Luckombe, P. (1800). *The Tablet of Memory, shewing every memorable event in history, from the earliest period to the year 1792*, 10th edn, London, J. Johnson and J. Walker

Lysons, D. and Lysons S. (1817). 'Topographical and historical account of Derbyshire', in *Magna Britannia*, London, Cadell, Strand and Greenland, vol. 5: 'Derbyshire'

Mabey, R. (1983). *Cold Comforts*, London, Hutchinson

McCarthy, J.J., Canziani, O.F., Leary, N.A., Dokken, D.J. and White, K.S. (2001). 'Climate Change 2001: Impacts, Adaptation, and Vulnerability', Contribution of Working Group II to the Third Assessment Report of the Intergovernmental Panel on Climate Change, Cambridge, Cambridge University Press

McDonnell, J. (ed.) (1963). *A History of Helmsley, Rievaulx and District*, York, Stonegate Press

Malden, H.E. (ed.) (1902–14). *The Victoria History of the County of Surrey*, 4 vols, London, Archibald Constable & Co.

Mannix and Whellan (1847). *History, Gazetteer, and Directory of Cumberland*, Beverley, W.B. Johnson

Markham, L. (1994). *The Derbyshire and Nottinghamshire Weather Book*, Newbury, Countryside Books

—— (1995). *The Lancashire Weather Book*, Newbury, Countryside Books

Marriott, W. and Gaster, F. (1886). 'The Floods of May 1886', *Quarterly Journal of the Royal Meteorological Society (Great Britain)* 12, 281–2

Marshall, W.A.L. (1952). 'The Lynmouth Floods', *Weather* 7 (11), 338–42

Matthew of Westminster (1570 edn). *Flores historiarum per Matthaeum Westmonasteriensem collecti*, 2 pts, London, T. Marsh

Melville, C.P., Levret, A., Alexandre, P., Lambert, J. and Vogt, J. (1996). 'Historical seismicity of the Strait of Dover – Pas de Calais', *Terra Nova* 8, 626–47

Met Office, UK (1944). *Monthly Weather Report of the Meteorological Office*, MO 467. 61(5), London, HMSO

—— (2004). *Flooding in North Cornwall – 16 August 2005*, Exeter, HMSO

Miyachi, M. (1992). 'Geological examination of the two old maps from the Tokugawa Era concerning the Shimabara Catastrophe', in T. Yanagi, H. Okada and K. Ohta (eds), *Unzen Volcano, the 1990–1992 eruption*, Kyushu, Nishinippon & Kyushu University Press

Money, W. (1905). *A Popular History of Newbury, in the County of Berks, from Early to Modern Times*, London, Simpkin, Marshall & Co

Moor, T. de la (1883 edn). *Vita et mors Edwardi secundi regis Angliae conscripta a Thoma de la Moor*, Rolls Series, London

Morley, E. (2005). 'Flooding (North-West). 11 Jan 2005', House of Commons Hansard Debates for 11 Jan 2005, column 201, London, United Kingdom Parliament, www.publications.parliament.uk, accessed August 2005

Muirhead, R. (2004). 'A rare hurricane in the South Atlantic: Hurricane Catrina March 2004', *Journal of Meteorology* UK 29 (294), 374–6

Naval Oceanography Command Centre (1979). *Annual Typhoon Report 1979* San Francisco, J.S. Naval Oceanography Command Centre/Joint Typhoon Warning Center

Newson, L. (1998). *The Atlas of the World's Worst Natural Disasters*, London, Dorling Kindersley

NOAA-NWS (2005a). 'Super Typhoon Tip', Fort Worth, TX, National Weather Service, www.srh.weather.gov/srh/jetstream/tropics/tip.htm, accessed August 2005

—— (2005b). 'Worldwide Tropical Cyclone Names', Camp Springs, MD, National Centers for Environmental Prediction, www.nhc.noaa.gov/aboutnames_history.shtml, accessed December 2005

Ogley, B., Currie, I. and Davison, M. (2000). *The Kent Weather Book*, Westerham, Kent, Froglets

Ordnance Gazetteer of Scotland: a survey of Scottish topography, statistical, biographical, and historical (1884–5). F.H. Groome (ed.), 6 vols, Edinburgh, Thomas C. Jack

Ormerod, G.W. (1891). *Rainfall at Teignmouth, 1878–1880 and 1886–1890*, held in the Royal Meteorological Society Collection, Devon Record Office, Exeter

Paris, M. (1866–9 edn). *Historia Anglorum sive ut vulgo dicitur Historia Minor*, 3 vols, Rolls Series, London

Pepys, S. (1904 edn). *The Diary of Samuel Pepys*, London, George Bell & Sons

Pielke, R.A., Klein, R. and Sarewitz, D. (2000). 'Turning the big knob: an evaluation of the use of energy policy to modulate future climate impacts', *Energy and Environment* 11, 255–76

Preston, A.E. (1929). *The Church and Parish of St. Nicholas, Abingdon*, London, Oxford University Press, pp. xiv, 507

Ralph of Coggeshall (1738 edn). 'Ex Radulphi Coggeshale Abbatis Chronico Anglicano', in M. Bouquet *et al.* (eds), *Recueil des Historiens des Gaules et de la France*, 24 vols, Paris, Palmé et Cie., tomes 13 and 18

Randi, J. (2005). *An Encyclopaedia of Claims, Frauds, and Hoaxes of the Occult and Supernatural*, v. 1995–2005, appendix III: 'Forty-Four End-of-the-World Prophecies – That Failed', Fort Lauderdale, FL, www.randi.org, accessed August 2005

Ravensdale, J.R. (1974). *Liable to Floods: Village Landscape on the Edge of the Fens, AD 450–1850*, Cambridge, Cambridge University Press

Reynolds, D.J. (1991). 'The weather in South Staffordshire 1739–1754 from the diary of Dr Richard Wilkes: Part 1: 1739–1740', *Journal of Meteorology* UK 16 (163), 299–305

Risk Management Solutions (2001). *Tropical Storm Allison, June 2001*, Event Report, Newark, CA, Risk Management Solutions Inc.

—— (2003). *December 1703 Windstorm 300 – Year Retrospective*, Risk Assessment Models Report, Newark, CA, Risk Management Solutions Inc.

Robert of Gloucester (1887 edn). *The Metrical Chronicle of Robert of Gloucester*, W.A. Wright (ed.), 2 vols, Rolls Series, London

Roger of Wendover (1841–4 edn) *Rogeri de Wendover Chronica, sive Flores Historiarum*, H.O. Coxe (ed.), 5 vols, London, English Historical Society

Russell, G.W.E. (1905). *Sidney Smith*, English Men of Letters series, v. 22 July

2004, Salt Lake City, UT, Project Gutenberg Literary Archive Foundation, http://library.beau.org/gutenberg/1/2/9/9/12994/12994-8.txt, accessed August 2005

Sampson, W. (1910 edn). *The Rector's Book, Clayworth, Notts*, Gill, H. and Guilford, E.L. (eds), Nottingham, H.B. Saxton

Sandt, K. (2004). 'Ivan Causes Region's Third Worst Flood', *Spanning the Gap* (the newsletter of Delaware Water Gap National Recreation Area) 26 (2)

Savage, R. and Fripp, E.I. (1921–2). *Minutes and Accounts of the Corporation of Stratford-Upon-Avon and Other Records 1553–1620*, Oxford, Oxford University Press

Scarth, A. (1999). *Vulcan's Fury: Man Against the Volcano*, New Haven, CT, Yale University Press

Seller, J. (1696). *The History of England*, London, John Gwillim

Shakespeare, W. (1906–9 edn). *The Complete Works of William Shakespeare*, the University Press Shakespeare, Renaissance edition, 40 vols, London, John Murray

Short, T. (1749). *A General Chronological History of the Air, Weather, Seasons, Meteors, &c. in Sundry Places and Different Times*, 2 vols, London, T. Longman

Simon of Durham (1855 edn). *The Historical Works of Simeon of Durham*, J. Stevenson (tr. and ed.), Church Historians of England, Pre-Reformation series, London, Seeleys, vol. 3, pt 2

Southall, H. (1895). 'Floods in the West Midlands', *Quarterly Journal of the Royal Meteorological Society* 21, 28–39

Stevenson, A. (1753–7). *The History of the Church and State of Scotland from the Accession of Charles I to the Restoration of Charles II*, 3 vols, Edinburgh

Stirling, R. (1997). *The Weather of Britain*, London, Giles de la Mare

Stratton, J.M. (1969). *Agricultural Records: AD 220–1968*, ed. R. Whitlock, London, John Baker

Stöffler, J. (1499). *Almanach noua plurimis annis venturis inseruientia*, Ulm, Joannis Reger

—— (1507–31). *Almanach noua plurimis annis venturis inseruientia: per Joannem Stoefflerinum Justinge sem Jacobum Pflaumen Ulmensem accuratissime supputata, etc. Petrus Liechtenstein: sub hemispherio Veneto*, Ulm, Jakob Pflaum

Sunday Express (1952). '39 lost in night of terror', 17 August 1952

Sutton, A. (1973). *A Story of Sidmouth*, 2nd edn, London, Phillimore

217

Symons, G.J. and Chatterton, S. (1895). 'The November Floods of 1894 in the Thames Valley', *Quarterly Journal of the Royal Meteorological Society* 21 (96), 193–8

Symons's Monthly Meteorological Magazine (1866–1920). Symons, G.J. (ed.) 54 vols, London, BRO/HMSO

Tacitus (1980 edn). *The Annals of Tacitus*, C.H. Moore (tr.), Cambridge, Loeb Classical Library

Treves, F. (1906). *Highways and Byways in Dorset*, London, Macmillan

Tyrrell, J. (1999). 'Unusual weather events, acts of God and legal liability', *Weather* 54 (2), 50–5

US Geological Survey (2005). *Summary of September 17–23, 2004, Flooding on the Delaware River and its Tributaries in New Jersey*, Trenton, NJ, USGS New Jersey Water Science Center

Vallee, D.R. and Dion, M.R. (1998). *Southern New England Tropical Storms and Hurricanes, a Ninety-eight Year Summary 1909–1997*, Taunton, MA, National Weather Service

Walker, J. (1772). 'An account of the irruption of Solway Moss', Philosophical Transactions of the Royal Society 62 (1772), 123–7

Wallis, J.E.W. (1923). *Whalley Abbey*, London, Society for Promoting Christian Knowledge

Walsingham, T. (1862 edn). *Thomae Walsingham . . . Historia Anglicana*, H.T. Riley (ed.), 2 vols, London, Longman, Green

Walter of Coventry (1873 edn). *The Historical Collections of Walter of Coventry*, W. Stubbs (ed.), London, Longman, vol. 2

Wang, D.W., Mitchell, D.A., Teague, W.J., Jarosz, E. and Hulbert, M.S. (2005). 'Extreme Waves Under Hurricane Ivan', *Science* 309 (5736), 896

Ward, A.W. (1935). *The Bridges of Shrewsbury*, Shrewsbury, Wilding & Son

Ward, S.N. and Day, S. (2001) 'Cumbre Vieja Volcano – Potential collapse and tsunami at La Palma, Canary Islands', *Geophysical Research Letters* 28 (17), 3397–400

Webb, J.D.C. and Meaden, G.T. (2000). 'Daily temperature extremes for Britain', *Weather* 55, 298–315

Webster, P.J., Holland, G.J., Curry, J.A. and Chang, H.R. (2005). 'Changes in Tropical Cyclone Number, Duration, and Intensity in a Warming Environment', *Science* 309 (5742), 1844–6

West, I.M. (2005). 'Chesil Beach: Storms and Floods' in I.M. West, *Geology of the Wessex Coast of Southern England*, Southampton, Southampton University, www.soton.ac.uk/~imw/chestorm.htm, accessed August 2005

Western Morning News (1952). 'How calamity came to the villages of Lynmouth and Barbrook', 18 August 1952

White, G. (1789). *The Natural History and Antiquities of Selborne, in the County of Southampton*, London, B. White and Son

—— (1795). *A Naturalist's Calendar, with Observations in various branches of Natural History*, ed. J. Aikin, London, B. & J. White

—— (1997 edn). *The Natural History of Selborne*, R. Mabey (ed.), Penguin Classics, London, Penguin

—— (1998 edn). *The Natural History of Selborne*, release date 1 August 1998, Salt Lake City, UT, Project Gutenberg Literary Archive Foundation, www.gutenberg.org/etext/1408, accessed August 2005

Williams, E. (1975). *Holmfirth: from Forest to Township*, Huddersfield, Advertiser Press

Wilson, I. (2001). *Before the Flood*, London, Orion

Withers, C.W.J. and McEwen, L.J. (1989). 'Historical records and geomorphological events: the Solway Moss "eruption" of 1771', *Scottish Geographical Magazine* 105 (3), 149–57

Yi Si (1998). 'The World's Most Catastrophic Dam Failures: the August 1975 Collapse of the Banqiao and Shimantan Dams', in Dai Qing, *The River Dragon Has Come!*, New York, M.E. Sharpe

Yongjian, D., Shiyin, L., Changwei, X., Yong, Z. and Jian, W. (2005). 'Yellow River at Risk', environmental impact assessment on the Yellow River source region by climate change, report to Greenpeace, October 2005, Greenpeace International, Netherlands

INDEX

Page numbers in bold indicate chapters; page numbers in italics refer to captions.